Rendezvous in Space

books by MARTIN CAIDIN

Rendezvous in Space

The Story
of
Projects
Mercury,
Gemini,
Dyna-Soar
and
Apollo

by
Martin Caidin

Drawings by
Fred L. Wolff

E. P. DUTTON & CO., Inc.
New York   1962

Published simultaneously in Canada by Clarke, Irwin &
Company Limited, Toronto and Vancouver

LIBRARY OF CONGRESS CATALOG CARD NUMBER: 62-14725

This book is for
GATHA COTTEE
an old friend,
who dreamed the dream

Contents

Illustrations

Photographs

Drawings and Diagrams

Acknowledgments

EVERY BOOK CARRIES in its words the unseen efforts of many people who gave readily of their assistance, and it is to many friends and associates that I am indebted for these pages. I am especially grateful for the invaluable assistance of Carolyn Baucom of the Office of Information, National Aeronautics and Space Administration, and also, in NASA, especially to Gatha Cottee, Jack King, Les Gaver, Paul Haney, Dick Mittauer, Bill Lloyd, Colonel "Shorty" Powers, Sally Gates—and to many others, to whom I offer my apologies for not adding their long list of names. As always, the skilled pen and brush of Fred L. Wolff adds life and meaning to the pages of this book. Vincent Vitollo and James Scrudato were always ready to assist—especially in our many travels high above the earth. Lt. Colonel "Tommy" Thompson, Lt. Colonel Ken Grine, Major John Whiteside, T/Sgt. Robert Bandy, Ken Senstadt, and the other members of the Air Force Office of Information, Air Force Missile Test Center, have always provided whatever assistance I have needed. Many of the "Canaveral Gang" have helped—Bill Harwood of Martin, Tom Heinsheimer of General Dynamics/Astronautics, Al Webb of UPI, Victor Vicks, Jim Atherton of UPI Photos, Hank Curth of the ready camera, and many, many more. And my very special gratitude to Bill Hines of the *Washington Evening Star*—a man with the rare gift of driving hard to the core of the story, and telling it in exciting fashion. To all those I have failed to mention by name—my apologies, and the explanation of my publisher reminding me that "there's just so much room." My thanks to one and all of you.

MARTIN CAIDIN

New York, 1962

All photos used through the courtesy of the National Aeronautics and Space Authority, with the exception of the following: Page 24, Bendix Corporation; Pages 28 and 33, Air Force; Page 66, Air Force Photo by Chuck Rogers; Page 79, Western Electric; Page 133 (top), Collins Radio; Pages 165, 168, 178, and 183, USSR Government; Page 186, Wide World Photos; Pages 274, 275 and 279, North American Aviation. The painting on Page 300 courtesy North American Aviation.

Rendezvous
in
Space

At exactly 9:47 a.m. the morning of February 20, 1962 . . . Atlas 109-D lifts from Complex Fourteen on Cape Canaveral to begin 300 seconds of powered flight . . . sending John H. Glenn into orbit.

The End of the Beginning

IT BEGINS EXACTLY at 47 minutes past nine o'clock the morning of February 20, 1962.

Until this moment powerful steel shackles clamp firmly about the base of a thick giant that stands 93 feet tall and weighs more than 264,000 pounds. The name of the giant is Atlas; her number is 109-D. She stands on a curving metal ring atop Complex Fourteen, on the edge of a wide sandpit known to the world as Cape Canaveral.

Perhaps it is not quite correct to say that Atlas 109-D stands on her launch ring. Several seconds before 9:47 a.m. the giant snarled into life. Two brilliant lances of fire spat from her flanks and cried out with a high, waspish scream. Now from her belly a volcano of flame gushes downward. The giant strains to break free of her shackles. But the clamps hold fast.

High above the fiery cascade, a man hears the swelling rumble of rocket thunder. His body responds to vibrations that sweep upward through the Atlas. His hand grips firmly but carefully an emergency control handle. In the lexicon of the new space age this is the "chicken switch." Should the rocket's flame escape its designed avenues, if fire dashes beyond its assigned channels, the man would pull swiftly on that handle. The response would be immediate—another, smaller gash of flame against the blue Florida sky.

And John Herschel Glenn, Jr., lieutenant colonel in the United States Marine Corps, one of seven astronauts of Project Mercury, would hurtle far above and to the side of Complex Fourteen. He would be gone in a spear of fire and a swath of smoke—

completely safe—even during the same moments that Atlas tears herself into blood-flame fragments. That is always the possibility of the age of space.

But not today. None of these things happens. At 47 minutes past nine o'clock, a series of instruments register in the green. The volcano is in full cry. Atlas thrusts back at the earth with all the energy her engineers imparted to her rounded flanks. The instruments are satisfied. They respond with an electronic nod, a spurt of current, and a command.

The steel shackles fly back. Atlas 109-D with her human passenger is free.

Spilling golden flame and violet plumes downward, the giant rejects the earth. With an "exhilarating surge" she begins to rush away from the planet that spawned her.

Three hundred seconds later a number of things have happened. The surface of the planet lies just more than 100 miles below the Atlas. The giant appears different. The flaring skirt about her base is gone. Her weight has changed; at 5,000° temperature her combustion chambers drained the superfine kerosene and supercold liquid oxygen that filled her steel tanks. Atlas ejected the propellants in a continuing stream of blazing gases. All told, the weight discarded in liquids, metal parts, and assemblies comes to more than 125 tons.

The velocity of Atlas is impressive. No longer does she point vertically into the sky; now she rushes horizontally above the surface of the world far below. Precisely at a height of 100.3 miles, Atlas 109-D is on the edge of the aerothermodynamic border of our planet's atmosphere. Considering all the factors of velocity and height and the density of the few remaining gases that ghost this far above earth, this is the edge of true space.

All this happens in the 300 seconds following the precise moment when the steel shackles back on Complex Fourteen cast free their prisoner.

Now the sequence of events continues. Explosive bolts crack hard; their sound booms with a hollow roar in the cavernous, emptied tanks of Atlas. Blue-white gases from the bolts sever clamp rings and metal connections and spring them free.

Exactly one more second winks into history. Three small rockets at the base of a bell-shaped capsule fire. Flame lances in vacuum.

Everything about space and flight through space is neat and precise and mathematical. The three rockets are called posigrades. Their plasticized substance burns with a measured thrust of 1,250 pounds.

At this moment the bell-shaped capsule—the name "Friendship 7" painted on its shingled sides—weighs exactly 2,987 pounds. The posigrades push the capsule with its lone human passenger away from the now-inert Atlas. The two objects in space separate with a speed of 24 feet per second. They will continue to drift apart, not only in distance but in destiny.

If the mathematics continue to be precise and an exhaustively computed schedule is maintained, the capsule will return hours from this moment—safely—to the surface of the earth. But Atlas 109-D is now debris. Her stainless steel sides reflect brilliantly in the morning sun of space. Her lines are beautiful. Her mass in orbit only a few years past would have represented a staggering feat. Nevertheless, she is still debris.

She is doomed to incineration when the earth begins to reclaim her bulk. The atmosphere that sustains life on the earth's surface is hostile to a five-ton mass plunging from space at 300 miles per minute. The meeting of Atlas 109-D and the thickening atmosphere will produce an inevitable result. There will be friction, a temperature of many thousands of degrees, and a silent funeral that will end in ashes.

But this is in the time to come. When the posigrades wink out, an electronic brain with sensitivity so great that it can measure the mass of a human hair, exercises its control. The brain senses, and considers, the movement of the capsule—its movement in *attitude*. Electronic commands open valves. Hydrogen peroxide snakes through fuel lines, bursts in carefully measured proportion and quantity from nozzles that are exposed to space.

The force exerted by the gas—which in the silence of space makes not even a sound outside the capsule—is negligible. But the conditions of space, of orbit, are totally alien to those of earth. The capsule no longer has any weight. It is falling around the earth. It has a specific *mass*, however, and the thrust of the jet nozzles is enough to swing the capsule around.

The one-and-a-half-ton spaceship does a half-turn. Where the man inside was facing in the direction of flight, now he faces backwards. The capsule tilts in response to its jets. Using the horizon far below as a reference line, the capsule tilts exactly 34 degrees above the horizon. Astronaut John Glenn now hurtles through space at five miles a second riding backwards and looking slightly down and toward where he has been.

This, however, is only of relative importance. What matters, really, is that at this moment the first American is in a perfect, wonderfully successful orbit about the planet earth. At this instant, the United States has come of age . . . in the technological age of space.

And this is extraordinarily important, because two men before John Glenn also experienced the miracle that he knows at this precise moment. Their names are Yuri Alekseyevich Gagarin and Gherman Stepanovich Titov. They are Russian cosmonauts; their spaceships were giants. Their performance was superb.

Before the flight through space of Astronaut John Glenn is complete, this 40-year-old Marine will be called upon to exercise his skill, his courage and patience in a manner unprecedented in history. For although the orbit is as close to perfect as might be desired, and the great Atlas has done its job in a fashion of which engineers dream, all will not be well.

John Glenn is the first human being to return to earth as a veteran of danger from malfunctioning of a vehicle in space. Mechanical difficulties will throw a grave, potentially lethal shadow on his ability to return safely to the surface of his world. Men will experience the cold hand of fear clutching at their hearts; in their compassion and the knowledge that John Glenn might be incinerated during his re-entry into the atmosphere, they will know even worse—their helplessness to assist the man far above them.

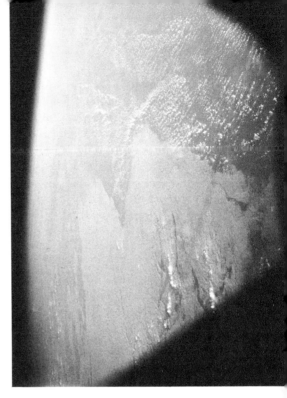

The earth from space . . . a view from a Mercury spacecraft of the west coast of Mexico during the early morning.

All these things, and more, are yet to happen. There will be moments of unutterable beauty, in which a veteran Marine, an experienced combat veteran, a man who has seen and done more than many average men, will look at the wonder of his world below him and cry out in delight at what he sees. There will be the glory of sunsets and dawns sweeping the planet earth, seeming to rush by at nearly 18,000 miles per hour. There will be the wonder of halos, of lightning flickering in storms a hundred miles below, of strange colors. There will be the eerie sight of thousands of tiny luminescent particles drifting ghostlike through the void of space with Astronaut Glenn, bringing another kind of wonder to us.

The flight of John Glenn will become science fiction come true in many ways, some unanticipated, as with the glowing particles above this planet. The sweep of sunrise and sunset in space is given to us through the words of our astronaut, but these are not unprecedented. They were spoken before, by Gagarin and Titov.

The flight of John Glenn was the fulfillment of dreams and hopes, the realization of long, hard work for which thousands of men still do not know—and likely never will know—the recognition earned by their labors. The flight of John Glenn is the culmination of plans made years past. And yet this, too, is not by itself the cause for the rejoicing that swept all America and much of the world as well.

There are many things which the first orbital flight of an American was not; there are many more which belong especially to us, his fellow citizens. No one writer said it better, with deeper understanding, with greater meaning, than one of the members of the press who was there on the day that Glenn struck a mark permanently in the calendar—a mark of which we are all so proud. James Reston wrote:[1]

> . . . it was the greatest American ride since Paul Revere, who didn't get a stamp 'til much later, and it was pure Americana from start to finish: part Hollywood spectacular, part circus, part county fair—three times around the world in living color and news from Heaven all the way.
>
> They say that this sort of thing has been done somewhere before, but not like this. Gagarin and Titov of the Soviet Union went into orbit by themselves, but Glenn made a party of it and took the whole country along for the ride.
>
> . . . America sort of needed an outing and an airing like this. For the first time in its history it had lately begun to second-guess itself. In fact, ever since Gagarin's first space flight, the skeptics and doubters, the witch-smellers and head-shrinkers, the debunkers and scoffers had confused and frustrated the country.
>
> This in turn produced a lot of big, splashy generalizations that somehow we had lost our way and had to find wholly new policies to deal with our problems at home and abroad.
>
> Even the American character, it was said, had changed. The old faiths and the old silent types with their plain wives and their beer and baseball were out of fashion, and then came along these matter-of-fact, uncomplicated, almost old-fashioned characters who paid more attention to outer space than to inner tensions and made the country begin to think again.

[1] *The New York Times,* February 20, 1962, dateline "Cape Canaveral."

This surely is what John Glenn did today. There was nothing fancy about him: just that flat Middle Western voice giving the facts, and saying he felt "real fine," and the view was "tremendous," and the coast of Africa was coming up on the left, and boy, the American shoreline sure looked wonderful.

This was the kind of talk you might hear from the nice man next door, which is about what most of these astronauts have turned out to be. . . .

A candid evaluation of the flight of Mercury-Atlas 6 on February 20, 1962, and that of Scott Carpenter in MA-7 on May 24, 1962, fail to carry the conviction that, great as they were, Glenn's and Carpenter's missions returned to the United States full parity in manned space flight with the Soviet Union. It is important for Americans to *understand* this harsh fact of life. In the unprecedented jubilation that swept America and brought open joy and relief to millions of people around the entire world, this fact sometimes becomes obscured.

Even a statistical comparison somewhat chills the celebration. That John Glenn's performance in our first manned orbital mission was superb—perhaps even greater—lies beyond question. No man could have done better.

But the very fact that he had to draw upon his wonderful skill both as a man and a test pilot underscores the reality of a spaceship that leaves much to be desired. Prior to Glenn's mission, two Mercury capsules had orbited the earth; one carried only instruments on a single pass around the world, the other a chimpanzee. The latter flight was programmed for an exact prelude to Glenn's scheduled time in space of three orbits. But this shot—MA-5—did not accomplish its goals. Mechanical difficulties with the Mercury spacecraft forced its premature return by command control from the ground with one orbit left to be flown. Glenn encountered serious problems with his attitude stabilization system by his second orbit; these difficulties continued through the remainder of the flight.

Thus on two successive missions a small spaceship that had undergone superb engineering, countless checkouts and examinations, failed to perform as designed. Had Glenn not been aboard the capsule, it would have been commanded to return at the close of the second orbit—a repeat of the flaws encountered in the previous mission. And there is a serious question if this successful return could have been accomplished.

The marvelous performance of Glenn emphasized in the most dramatic of terms the intrinsic ability of *man* in any space system. It was a rousing vindication of the claims of many of our top scientists and engineers, who criticized bitterly their associates for too great an enchantment with the machine and who condemned the man as useless in space. The end result is the realization that our equipment leaves much to be desired in terms of space vehicles.

The flights of Mercury-Atlas 6 with Astronaut John H. Glenn, Jr., and Mercury-Atlas 7 with Scott Carpenter, did not return to the United States the leadership or the initiative in space. They did not give to this country even a full parity with the USSR. Glenn's and Carpenter's space flights did serve notice that we were back in the space race, driving hard; this is the key fulfillment of the missions to the people of the United States, and to our friends around the world.

Ten months before that morning of February 20, 1962, Yuri Gagarin orbited the earth in a spaceship that weighed 10,416 pounds. His was but a single sweep around the earth—a preliminary exploration.

But it *was* the *first* manned orbital flight. It prompted Congressman David S. King of the House Committee on Science and Astronautics to state that: "We are in a game in which there are no prizes for second place as far as I can see. Everybody knows about Charles Lindbergh but who . . . knows who made the second flight across the Atlantic Ocean? I am very sorry myself that one of our own men did not have that honor. This man Gagarin . . . is the one that will go down in the history books. More power to him, but I would have wished devoutly it could have been one of our own men."

Six months before Glenn captured the plaudits of men everywhere, Gherman Titov rocketed into space within a spaceship that also weighed more than 10,000 pounds. *Vostok II* was more than 20 feet long. It carried television cameras, radios, extensive

Lt. Colonel John H. Glenn, Jr., US Marine Corps . . . fighter pilot, combat veteran of two wars, first American astronaut to orbit the earth.

scientific equipment. It carried enough food, water, oxygen, power, air purification equipment, control systems fuel, and other items to last for a flight of at least ten *days*.

Vostok II's was the first space *journey* ever made. A human being traveled in one flight lasting 25 hours and 18 minutes a distance from the earth to the moon and back again. He went to sleep for a period of time almost twice as great as the entire time that our first man in orbit, Glenn, spent in space.

By comparison, *Friendship 7,* much smaller than the Russian spaceship, weighed only 3,000 against more than 10,000 pounds. *Friendship 7* was severely limited in its ability to support Glenn in space for even less than 24 hours. The weight and space problems in the Mercury capsule were so critical that every pound literally had to be accounted for. The Mercury capsule in the MA-5 and MA-6 flights in orbit encountered serious mechanical difficulties.

Facts such as these—by themselves—are hardly an impetus to rejoicing.

But the performances of Glenn and Carpenter—that is entirely another matter. Theirs were deeds that evoked open admiration, and immediate congratulations, from the Soviet cosmonauts. They, more than all other men, understand to what extent Glenn and Carpenter were called upon to perform in space.

There are many other things of which we can be proud. Although we must suffer by comparison of equipment and power against the space vehicles of the USSR, this is not the entire picture. Project Mercury first began some three and a half years before Glenn ascended from the earth atop a ball of golden fire. We have—in full view of the comparisons—come a long way.

The mission of Mercury-Atlas 6 more than anything else, even more than Glenn's feat in space, emphasized the existence of a great, closely knit team. Our first orbital flight evolved from an organization of men whose overriding, compelling objective was a successful flight of an American in orbit.

With this as experience, as fact, the way to the future could become clear. Thus we are able to chart our course more firmly,

with greater knowledge—a process impossible before February
20, 1962. Those four hours and 56 minutes of Mercury-Atlas 6
were not a goal unto themselves.

They were the first step—that, and no more.

One American in orbit is a miracle.

Two Americans in orbit is . . . statistical.

The mission of Astronaut John Glenn was but the end of the
beginning.

1: *Test of Patience*

On April 9, 1961, one of the scientists attending an international conference of space-flight activities was besieged by reporters. The scientist was Academician Leonid I. Sedov of the USSR Academy of Sciences. From the very beginning of the Russian space program in 1954, Sedov had been a key figure and a decision-maker who had helped the Soviets develop their massive rocket boosters and satellites.

The reporters asked Sedov why the Soviet government insisted upon keeping the names of their cosmonauts a secret from the world. Sedov smiled at the newsmen. "We don't give the names," he said, "because they may decide not to go." Then the smile faded.

"Besides—the publicity may interfere with the program."

Three days later Yuri Gagarin raced around the world at 18,000 miles per hour.

By the close of 1961 the roar of the rocket booster that sent Gagarin into orbit had faded to a whisper. But not the words of Leonid I. Sedov. In December of 1961 Sedov's remarks began to assume special meaning. By January of 1962 they were beginning to haunt Cape Canaveral. By mid-February they were a ghost chasing down the corridors of the headquarters building in Washington, D.C., of the National Aeronautics and Space Administration.

More than one government official was entertaining thoughts that perhaps the United States might have well adopted an attitude of less publicity and more prudence in opening the

Hoisting capsule to Atlas gantry

gates to Cape Canaveral for Mercury-Atlas 6—the planned first orbital flight of an American astronaut.

Despite the denials of government officials, the United States wanted desperately to send an American into orbit before the year 1961 came to its end. If we could have accomplished this feat, then the official yearbooks would have shown that both the Soviet Union and the United States achieved manned orbital flight in the same year. The record books would have balanced a bit more, despite the sensational 17-orbit mission of Titov in August, 1961.

More optimistically than realistically, the earliest possible launching date for Mercury-Atlas 6 was set for December 19. In truth, there was virtually no hope that this could be even remotely realized. In the previous unmanned orbital flights of the Mercury capsule, the time the Atlas booster flights spent on the launch ring was measured not in days or weeks but in months.

The NASA operational plan called for Atlas 109-D to be

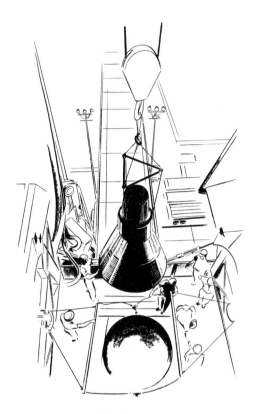

placed on Complex Fourteen with a minimum time of approximately six weeks to go before the attempted manned launch. About four or five weeks before launch the capsule is mated to its booster.

But the time period between erecting the booster to the launch ring and the actual date of firing is something affected by thousands of different factors. Any one of them individually, and more often they come collectively than as a single item, can force delays in the countdown.

Atlas 109-D went on Complex Fourteen on December 1, 1961. It didn't take long for the official announcement to come that the United States would *not* attempt a launching until the following year. NASA scheduled MA-6 for January.

They never made it. Five times in January Mercury-Atlas 6

Mercury-Atlas 6 space vehicle: the Atlas 109-D booster, the Mercury space-craft, and the spacecraft escape tower and rocket. Weight at launching: approximately 265,000 pounds.

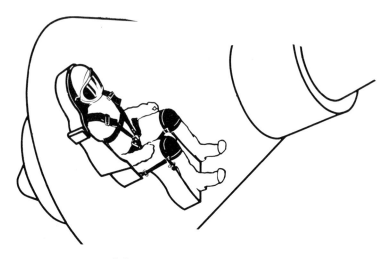

Pilot's restraint system in Mercury capsule

suffered a series of disappointing delays. A faulty gyro had to be replaced in the Atlas; then, it was necessary to work on another major engineering item (a broken servo cam). The capsule sprang some leaks and displayed a faulty oxygen valve. Those caused more scrubs.

On January 27 the mechanical and technical problems were gone. Atlas 109-D was ready. Capsule No. 13 was ready. All of Cape Canaveral, all the world-wide tracking stations, all the recovery area forces, everything was ready or, as the word has it at Canaveral, everything was in a *Go* condition.

Everything, that is, except the weather. It was foul.

America's first manned orbital flight was postponed to February 1. The booster fuel tank sprang a leak. In the intermediate bulkhead, which separates the liquid oxygen and the kerosene tank, there is a small cavity filled with styrofoam. In a routine check engineers discovered that kerosene fuel had leaked into the insulating material. Another postponement.

Before John Glenn would reach his moment with destiny 100 miles above the earth, his mission would go through nine major postponements and delays for a variety of reasons.

The Mercury capsule—which for Glenn's mission weighed 2,987 pounds in orbit—is a one-and-a-half-ton package of poten-

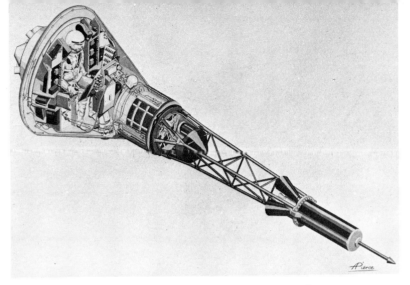

The complete Mercury spacecraft—orbital weight minus the escape tower and rocket for MA-6: 2,987 pounds.

tial trouble. This is no deprecation of its design, its designers, or its builders; the very fact that they could create in a bell-shaped machine only nine and a half by six feet an actual spaceship is virtually a technological miracle in itself.

The capsule interior is about the size of a telephone booth, and this is a booth with equipment, dials, meters, controls, power devices, and a thousand other items crammed into every available cubic inch of space. In front of the pilot is his main instrument panel. On a console to the left, as well as in the center, are the navigational and control instruments. The pilot also has his optical viewer for his periscope (which protrudes from the capsule in orbit) in the center. On the right section of the main panel are environmental system gauges and controls, a battery of electrical switches, instrument dials and meters, and an elaborate radio communications system. Altogether, the capsule that Glenn would ride into space has well over 100 lights, fuses, switches, and varying controls and display facilities.

Squeezed neatly beneath the panel and control system in "flight position" is the astronaut's couch of crushable honeycomb material bonded to a fiberglass shell. This is lined with rubber padding. About the couch is a restraint system.

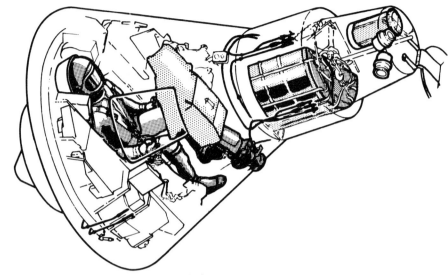

MA-6 spacecraft system

Ready for flight, Glenn is virtually a "captive" of his *Friendship 7*. Across his body goes a shoulder and a chest strap, leg straps, crotch strap, lap belt, and toe guards.

In flight, to control the attitude of his spaceship, Glenn used a special system of 18 different reaction-thrust nozzles that are located about the capsule surface. From fuel tanks within the spacecraft, hydrogen peroxide is used to create steam of specifically measured thrust. Some nozzles fire with only one-pound thrust, others with 24 pounds.

It's a complicated system, not at all enhanced by the use of hydrogen peroxide, which more than one engineer at the Cape has described to me as "corrosive and troublesome beyond forgiving." A flight in the capsule means a host of control problems —attitude in orbit, attitude during the moment of firing the retrorockets, damping out oscillations during the critical re-entry maneuver, and being able to recover from tumbling maneuvers.

In orbit, the capsule is weightless and likely to wander about on its three axes—pitch (up and down), yaw (side to side), and roll about its axis (like an airplane in level flight but rolling its wings around and around). Space flight snarls these normally complicated control problems by introducing the possibility of tumbling, when the capsule may move *simultaneously* through all three axes!

To maintain attitude control through this regime of flight, Glenn has an automatic pilot that is programed before the flight to maintain desired attitudes and to go through special, necessary maneuvers. But this isn't enough (as the actual flight would show in chilling fashion), and so Glenn also has three manual attitude-control systems. A "fly-by-wire" arrangement allows him to control the capsule attitude by providing a direct "override" linkage through the automatic pilot; there are also a direct manual system, which works through mechanical linkages to the manual-control fuel system, and a rate-command system which also uses the manual fuel system.

To operate these systems the capsule has a control stick— much like that of a fighter airplane—which creates the desired effect of attitude control by causing the jet nozzles outside the

Three-axis motions of Mercury capsule

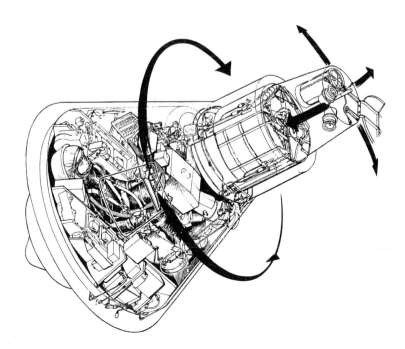

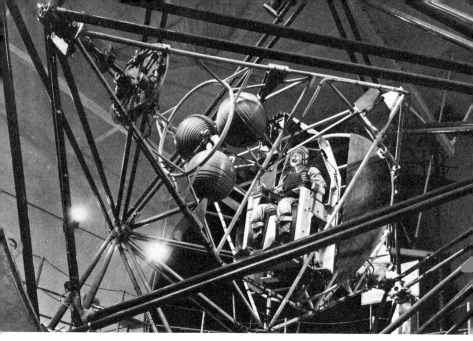

With these training simulators (MASTIF, top, and ALFA, below), Mercury astronauts practiced reaction and attitude controls and attitudes of orbital flight.

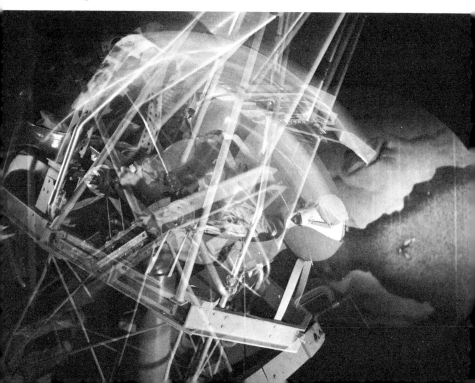

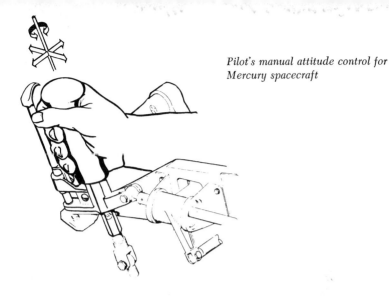

capsule to discharge their hydrogen-peroxide gas. When Glenn moves the stick back and forth, he exercises movement in pitch. When he moves the stick from side to side, he has roll control. Both these maneuvers follow the control movements of those in an airplane. Rotating the stick adds a yaw control for sideways motion, which *doesn't* have a parallel in an airplane. In the latter the pilot uses rudder controls that are operated by foot pressure.

Whatever the details—and they become endless—controlling the attitude of the capsule under zero gravity conditions can be a frustrating experience. It demands—as Glenn and the other astronauts have had—extraordinary practice, and then countless hours of more practice.

The heart of the entire system is the hydrogen-peroxide fuel linkage to the nozzles, which in turn are activated by the control stick. Add to the normal complications the fact that the hydrogen peroxide is so corrosive as to give engineers gray hair, and countdown delays come to be anticipated as normal—while countdowns without delays caused by this system are almost startling.

Another item to keep engineers awake at night and to introduce additional delays into a countdown is the life-environment system of the capsule. This is of critical interest to the man who

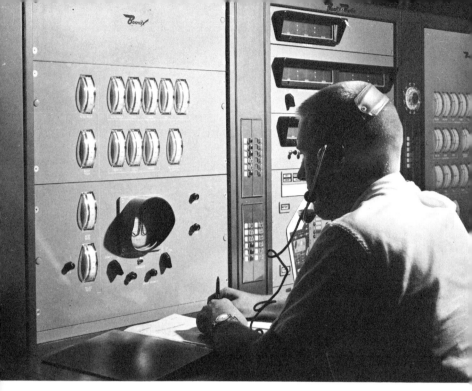

Doctors and "aeromedical observers" on duty at the 18 stations of the Mercury global tracking network kept a complete running physical profile on John Glenn during his orbital flight—including such items as body temperature, suit temperature, respiration and pulse rates, oxygen supply, and a cardioscope report of heartbeat.

squeezes his spacesuited body into the "crowded telephone booth," for if this system fails to operate properly, then there isn't any need to worry about anything—ever again. The system must provide breathing oxygen, ventilate the astronaut's body, remove metabolic products, keep the cabin temperature within comfortable and safe limits from an outside temperature level of 100° below zero to *three thousand degrees* above, assure that the entire control cabin and the pilot's suit are fully pressurized as needed, operate under forces ranging from 20 times that of normal gravity to the total absence of gravity—and finally, be able to do all this automatically, or under a manual override.

This life-environment system, therefore, briefly deserves our special attention. Actually there are two systems—one for the cabin and the second for the suit. Both operate simultaneously, using oxygen, coolant water, and electrical devices. Spherical bottles squeezed into a space between the pilot's feet hold the oxygen. The water system is more complicated. Coolant water is held in a tank with a pressurized bladder system for the flow of water into a heat exchanger during zero gravity flight.

The pilot himself becomes a part of this system. To enable doctors on the earth to monitor his physical status, the astronaut is taped about his body with biosensor leads. These come together at an outlet above the right thigh of the suit, and everything is then plugged neatly into a single unit. This in turn leads to special instruments that convert the physiological processes of the astronaut into electronically coded signals that are telemetered by radio to a station beneath the capsule. There the process continues its amazing path, and the signals appear before doctors as intelligible squiggles and lines on charts and graphs.

Ventilating the astronaut's body is vital; there's an inlet port in the suit located at the torso with an outlet port on the helmet. Oxygen enters the suit at the torso to distribution ducts. These force the air to all parts of the body, and then into the helmet. Part of the air is then breathed; the remainder is used to remove carbon dioxide and water.

The gaseous mixture removed from the suit must be filtered automatically of any particles of matter. Then the gases pass into a chemical canister of activated charcoal and lithium hydroxide, which scrubs the gases clean of carbon dioxide. The remaining gas is then cooled by a water evaporation-type heat exchanger which uses the natural vacuum of space to cause the coolant water to boil at the conveniently low temperature of only 35° Fahrenheit.

The life-environment system contributes its share to the many lights, dials, switches, and controls of the capsule. It is, like the attitude-control system, an ingenious and intricate maze woven with exacting care through the limited space of the Mercury vehicle.

Both the attitude-control and the life-environment systems were involved in the continuing delays and postponements in Mercury-Atlas 6.

In the capsule are electrical power supplies, inverters, exchangers, solenoids, valves, switches, controls, pyrotechnic devices, dials, buttons, rockets, fuel supplies, bolts, nuts, screws, assemblies—*ad infinitum*. They form the meticulously intricate fabric of the spacecraft.

Behind this small vehicle for flight out of this world lie the efforts of more than 15,000 people who have labored and sweated to produce the spacecraft. Their labors would have been made infinitely simpler had there been greater size, volume, and weight in the specifications that were dictated for the Mercury capsule. But these elements were sorely limited, and so a force of engineers, scientists, technicians, administrators, pilots and air crews, physicists, and a wide spectrum of industrial and laboratory workers, to some minor or full-time extent, worked for four years to produce the one and a half tons of Mercury spacecraft. In the line of capsules that moved slowly from the factory of the McDonnell Aircraft Corporation in St. Louis, Missouri, No. 13 was selected for a flight with a man yet unnamed, unselected but anxious to be—John Glenn.

The cost from the first contract let in 1958 to the morning of February 20, 1962, is somewhat staggering—$160,000,000.

Capsule No. 13 arrived at Cape Canaveral exactly 166 days before Glenn rode the spacecraft away from this planet. During that time engineers probed, studied, checked, partially dissected, tested, repaired, and tested again the bell-shaped machine that would keep a man alive and functioning in space, and then bring him safely back to the world of mortal, earthbound men. The official "No. 13" vanished into technical limbo as paintbrushes were wielded diligently to apply the name selected by Glenn— "Friendship 7"—to the side of the capsule. There were also the brilliant words UNITED STATES and a painting of the American flag.

During the 166 days at Cape Canaveral, Capsule No. 13 went through no less than 255 design changes.

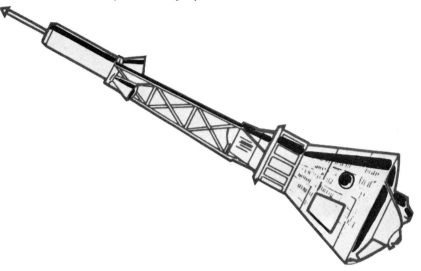

To assure proper operation of the automatic stabilization and control system (ASCS), engineers installed a new automatic pilot with "logic circuitry" added to the system. They added new fuses to the rate gyro power leads. To keep a constant temperature of 75° F. on the ASCS scanners, they placed heat blankets on the scanners.

In the reaction-control system, the engineers found it necessary to make some other changes. The automatic thrust chamber solenoid valves were equipped with plastic flare seals when the capsule arrived at the Cape; the plastic units were removed, and in their place were substituted soft aluminum washers. Beryllium heat sinks were installed on both the manual and automatic roll thruster assemblies.

The electrical system produced more than its share of headaches. The engineers removed fuses from the manual standby inverter (which converts DC current to AC), reinforced the fuse holders, and put the whole works together again. Because of troubles with past capsules, they added indicator warning lights to the inverters, and gained some additional reliability by

During painstaking and exhaustive checkout of a Mercury capsule in Hangar S on Cape Canaveral, technicians examine, test, and check out every single item—sometimes many times over. This is the capsule flown by Alan Shepard.

installing an auxiliary battery for the wiring of the maximum altitude sensor.

Special precautions were taken to prevent the escape tower rocket (a unit looming 16 feet above the capsule) from jettisoning ahead of its scheduled release time.

This emergency escape system itself came in for heated discussion at Cape Canaveral. As the weeks passed by with mounting frustration—for all concerned—it became apparent that the task of investigating the intricacies of booster and capsule, so as fully to inform the public, was indeed a complex one. The escape system was a prime example.

Atop the Mercury spacecraft is a tripod steel tower 16 feet

Mercury-Atlas 3 exploding, with capsule escape

high and weighing 900 pounds. At the top of the tower there's an escape rocket—one rocket with three nozzles—that in an emergency will fire for exactly seven-tenths of a second. But since this rocket (which is designed for reliability above all, and has never failed in a test) has a thrust of 50,000 pounds, its kick is great enough to haul the capsule from a position on the ground to a half-mile into the air. If it fires during ascent, it pulls the capsule at least 1,000 feet above the climbing booster rocket.

If the flight is normal, then the tower jettisons from the capsule about 154 seconds after launch. A second small rocket (17 inches long by six inches wide) with a thrust of 860 pounds burns for one and a half seconds to apply a "side push" to the escape-tower system during the jettison process, which involves the firing of both the escape rocket and the jettison rocket to pull the tower assembly away from the capsule.

But the heart of the system is its ability to lift the capsule away from the booster in the event of explosion or failure. During the flight upward from the earth, the astronaut's safety is assured by an electronic watchdog called ASIS (Abort Sensing and Implementation System). ASIS weighs a compact 36 pounds, and it has the ability to sense electronically the operation of all the Atlas subsystems, such as the motors, hydraulics, pressure lines, temperatures, and so forth. If these systems work properly, ASIS remains quiet. If they go wrong—a line ruptures, flame blossoms out—ASIS whips into action in time measured in thousandths of a second. Immediately ASIS commands the heavy escape rocket atop the capsule tower to fire and pull the spacecraft to safety. Three seconds later TNT bricks in strategic locations within the booster tear the Atlas to shreds.

The Range Safety Officer (RSO) on Cape Canaveral also can order the escape rocket to fire. The Atlas may veer off course, endangering life and property on the ground. If this happens, then the RSO—who watches all this on an electronic display in a room at Cape Canaveral—flicks his famous DESTRUCT button. A radio signal to the Atlas informs the booster to "commit suicide." But before the explosive charges go off, ASIS is already in the act. ASIS blocks for several seconds the command for self-destruction. It receives the destruct signal, realizes that there's trouble, fires the escape rocket, and then, three seconds later, joins the Atlas in a blast of mushrooming fire.

It's quite a system and in past emergencies (unmanned flights) it has worked perfectly.

But there's a hitch here. The ASIS watchdog is kept asleep, so to speak, until a *first motion of two inches.* In other words, until the Atlas actually lifts a minimum of two inches from its launch ring, the ASIS is kept inoperative.

What happens in an emergency before these first two inches of flight? Is the system of escape and survival automatic? If there is trouble aboard the Atlas while the astronaut is in the capsule, can the pilot simply yank down hard on the abort handle (the "chicken switch") and so cause the escape rocket to fire?

We had believed so, but at a press meeting held at NASA Press Headquarters in Cocoa Beach, Florida, one engineer indicated that in effect Glenn did not have this abort capability on the ground. It seemed that before the escape rocket would fire, the umbilical (power cable) would first have to be ejected from the Atlas, to which it is normally attached until about 35 seconds before takeoff, and that the command to eject the umbilical must be initiated on the ground.

So I wrote a news story, datelined "Cape Canaveral," emphasizing all these points, and that Astronaut Glenn didn't have completely automatic escape-system protection on the ground.

I wanted to be absolutely certain of accuracy. Several engineers from General Dynamics/Astronautics (the company that builds the Atlas and the ASIS system) checked the contents. Their reaction was scathing.

The first engineer had been mistaken, explained one of them, or else his meaning had not gotten across clearly. "We realized," explained the General Dynamics expert, "that an on-the-pad abort might be necessary, and we built in a sensing system for this.

"If Glenn pulled the abort handle—let's say six minutes before launch time—the signal would flash in the blockhouse, in Mercury Control, and on other indicator panels. He isn't going to keep quiet at such a moment; likely he'd call out 'Abort!' or some other signal. At that instant a man—any man in several different locations—hits the abort command signal. It takes only a second or two for this reaction to occur; we know, because we've tested it many times.

"At the instant that switch is hit in any one of several command places, the abort process is *Go.* The umbilicals are still attached; there's an interlock in the system that prevents the escape rocket from igniting. The abort system senses this interlock, and commands the umbilicals to eject. If this doesn't happen, *instantly,* the abort system *overrides the interlock.* In a fraction of a second the igniter in the escape rocket is alive; the rocket fires and hauls the capsule off the Atlas with the umbilicals connected. . . ."

But this movement also exerts a specific pressure on the umbilical connections. The moment this pressure level is reached, the umbilicals are automatically released—and the movement of the capsule pulls them free, snaps them away from the capsule so that there is no interference with the escape process.

It's all very neat, and Astronaut Glenn *does* have that wonderful electronic web all about him to assure his protection.

The only link in the entire process that is not automatic is the ASIS electronic watchdog during the time it is not "alive" in terms of its sensing abilities—that is, prior to those first two inches of movement of the Atlas during liftoff. During this time, the escape sequence can be initiated by the astronaut in the capsule, by Mercury Control, or by the blockhouse.

But it took a long time to find out just what was going on!

During the long countdowns and the repeated delays, the General Dynamics/Astronautics engineers checked their ASIS system over with the finest of examinations. They couldn't afford anything less than nitpicking, microscopic examination of a system that is both delicate and intricate. Not once, however, did the ASIS system require a hold or a delay in the countdown, a ringing tribute to its engineers.

Remember the life-environment system we discussed? Even something as simple as the "chemical scrubber" to cleanse the air of carbon dioxide within the capsule added a delay to the countdown.

The first "official" launch date for MA-6 was January 16. On that day a defect in the air-conditioning and circulation system of the capsule showed up, and it took a week to get everything back in shape. Or so the engineers thought. By the end of the week they still weren't ready and another postponement was called. NASA announced a new planned firing date.

We went close to the wire on this one. Then, the day before the newly scheduled shot, the engineers found a faulty oxygen

During repeated missions scrubs and postponements, Astronaut Glenn "honed the edge" by flying many simulated missions in the Mercury spacecraft Procedures Trainer at Cape Canaveral.

regulator in the capsule. That took more time, and another postponement.

Considerably later, events began to converge in terms of delays and postponements. On one scheduled shot morning, technical holds delayed the countdown. The weather was perfect. But by the time the booster/capsule system was ready to go, the weather wasn't perfect any longer.

The count went really close this time, but a thick blanket of clouds moved in and loomed darkly over the Cape. The word came through once again, with its wearying overtone, that the shot was scrubbed.

What drove everyone to distraction during those long weeks at Canaveral was the need to juggle and balance a host of factors to meet all-too-rare moments when *everything* was ready for a firing. On one occasion a scrub because of weather forced a delay of several days. This startled the reporters, to whom Colonel John "Shorty" Powers of NASA explained that technicians would have "to change the carbon-dioxide absorbing material in the capsule since it has been used so much in preflight checkouts."

This begins a chain reaction. All the equipment involved with the chemicals to absorb carbon dioxide must be checked and preflighted once again. But this meant a delay in which engineers had to "stand down" other equipment. This added more delays. By this time the launch crews were on the point of exhaustion, and *they* needed a rest.

Keep this up, and soon the recovery force of 15,000 men aboard the Navy's units at sea begin to run out of fuel, and their supplies have to be replenished.

It *was* kept up—and the days stretched out into weeks, and one postponement after the other.

The Balky Booster

Through most of this ulcer-producing period the great Atlas booster stolidly absorbed a beating for which it was never designed. The Atlas-D is originally a weapon—an intercontinental ballistic missile. As such, it was not designed to endure on so many occasions the prodding, poking, dissection, testing, fueling, defueling, pressurizing, depressurizing, and thousands of other activities that went on at the Cape.

In short, it is a weapon first, and a space-vehicle booster second. It has had a remarkably outstanding record in its latter role, but the facts of life as they involve the Atlas were quickly forgotten in the rising impatience at the continuing delays at Canaveral. Many newsmen, frantic for "different" copy and grimly in pursuit of villains on whom to pin the "blame" for the delays, took after the Atlas like a pack of hounds in full cry. American citizens who read this material soon began to wonder if the Atlas wasn't simply a boondoggle, and their feelings on the matter weren't enhanced when Congressman James G. Fulton of Pennsylvania leaped nimbly into the spotlight to condemn the Atlas as a rocket fit only for the scrap heap. The fact that the Congressman's comments were so devoid of engineering accuracy or competence as to be worthless did not lessen the widespread attention he received.

As a space booster the Atlas has performed remarkably well. On many occasions when an Atlas-boosted space mission has failed, the accusing finger that pointed at the Atlas also failed to note that the first-stage operation was perfect—and that the upper stages had not operated as planned. That the Atlas and the first stage were one and the same often missed comment.

There were three orbital attempts with the Atlas-D booster prior to the flight of Glenn. MA-3 in April of 1961 ended in a spectacular, fiery blast high over Cape Canaveral. That day I watched pieces of Atlas rain down along the beaches. Did the Atlas explode? No; she had been destroyed deliberately. The great rocket ascended perfectly. But as the Atlas climbs, she must also roll in her ascent and bend into a particular heading of flight.

Somewhere in the guidance system an electronic component failed. The rocket was working perfectly, but the guidance system did not command the booster to roll and turn. In Central Control at Cape Canaveral, the Range Safety Officer noticed the delay in programing. He had no choice; he closed a switch.

The ASIS system aboard the booster flashed into operation. The unmanned Mercury capsule whipped up and away in a streak of flame and smoke. Seconds later a mushrooming ball of flame engulfed the Atlas, result of the deliberate detonation of the TNT bricks.

Engineers placed this same capsule atop another Atlas, and assigned the new shot the designation of MA-4.

The Atlas performance this time was—literally—flawless. The capsule whirled around the earth in a single orbit, in a flight that engineers said was "as perfect as was possible to achieve."

Then came MA-5 in which the chimpanzee Enos had its stab at fame. The Atlas once again operated in as perfect a fashion as could be hoped for.

The Atlas has also turned in stellar performances as the booster for the early Ranger probes and for the Midas and Samos satellites. Indeed, the most perfect orbit ever achieved for the country, with the Midas satellite, came from an Atlas-boosted firing.

But during the preparations for MA-6, the word came that the Atlas booster 109-D had encountered serious difficulties in the countdown and that the mission would be once again delayed for a long period because of the need to effect major repairs on the Atlas. The aluminum membrane of the bulkhead between the kerosene and liquid-oxygen tanks had ruptured. Fuel had poured through; a launch might have—likely would have—resulted in a disastrous explosion. Many newsmen were quick to drag the Atlas onto the guillotine of public opinion. At first glance they could not be blamed, for major repairs to the Atlas *were* necessary.

The story of how Atlas 109-D was rushed into proper shape for MA-6 in an unbelievably brief time is one of the great events behind the scenes of the flight of John Glenn.

In the big Atlas rocket the liquid-oxygen and kerosene tanks are separated by a strong stainless steel bulkhead. At the bottom of the bulkhead are a thin aluminum membrane and styrofoam insulation. The purpose of the styrofoam is to insulate the kerosene tanks against the supercold liquid oxygen (which is at such low temperature that it boils at $297°$ F. *below* zero). The membrane had ruptured, and the kerosene had soaked heavily into the styrofoam.

Had this ever happened before in the Atlas program? Yes, it had. Back in October of 1960, Atlas 55-D was on the launch pad, almost ready for firing. During the fueling operation things began to get out of hand. Internal pressure within the Atlas tanks built up excessively; at the same time an excess of fuel poured into the tank. The aluminum membrane ruptured. The 80-pound styrofoam blanket soaked up an additional 160 pounds of fuel.

This mishap by itself would perhaps not have been critical (although some engineers argued this point). What made it dangerous was the flight pattern of the Atlas. At an acceleration of nine g, the 240 pounds of kerosene-soaked styrofoam would weigh over 2,100 pounds. A normal weight of 80 pounds of styrofoam would suddenly become in excess of a ton. Engineers said that there was a great chance that at this point the membrane and the styrofoam would collapse into the fuel tank. Styrofoam particles might enter the turbopumps of the propulsion system—and that would end up with the Atlas tearing itself to pieces in flight.

To repair 55-D, General Dynamics/Astronautics went to considerable trouble. They removed the giant rocket from its launch stand, carried it back to the hangar. There, engineers dismantled the mounts for the three powerful engines and removed the engines. They pulled down the aft bulkhead. Then they peeled off the styrofoam.

Now they had a missile without the insulation blanket. But was this styrofoam really necessary to the Atlas in flight? Despite the earlier conviction of its need, nothing had ever shown up to support the continued use of the styrofoam. The Air Force and General Dynamics/Astronautics made a decision on the spot to fly Atlas 55-D without the styrofoam. That was one way to check out the theory that it could be removed.

On October 22, 1960, Atlas 55-D "went all the way" down the Atlantic Missile Range. And an accident became a blessing in disguise. The Air Force decided then and there to eliminate the styrofoam in all Atlas E and F combat missiles. It simply wasn't needed, and the rocket as a result was 80 pounds lighter.

The problem with Glenn's booster came from the fact that this was a D-model Atlas; as used with the Mercury and Ranger (moon and deep space probe) programs the styrofoam liners were simply left in place. The engineers didn't believe it was necessary to modify the D-series boosters.

Then came mid-January of 1962 and a scheduled firing with Ranger III, a powerful lunar probe in which the Atlas is the first stage and an Agena B serves as Stage II. This combination is powerful enough to send a payload of 675 pounds away from the earth with a speed of 25,000 miles per hour.

In the pre-launch check, engineers discovered the situation they had known before with Atlas 55-D; the styrofoam was soaked with kerosene. There's a time problem in launching a probe to the moon; each month has a prime firing time of only a few days. If Ranger III was to get off the ground in January, the repairs had to be made immediately.

General Dynamics/Astronautics engineers performed one of the most ingenious repair jobs in missile history. Instead of dismantling the entire bottom section of the Atlas, they left the rocket standing on its launch ring and dumped all the kerosene. The engineers worked as a team co-ordinated with all the precision of a fine watch. They removed the center sustainer motor with all its plumbing—pumps, fuel lines, connections, and auxiliary equipment. To the astonishment of veteran engineers on Canaveral, the General Dynamics/Astronautics team didn't touch the powerful two outboard combustion chambers. Instead, they went right up through the space created by removal of the sustainer. The bottom of the kerosene tank is shaped like the end of a cone. At a point where the tank bottom is just two feet in diameter the engineers removed a cap.

All skills are needed in the space age. Two company carpenters worked against time to build a scaffolding inside the bottom of the fuel tank. They built a series of vertical supports inside the tank and placed a work platform atop the supports. Then they repeated the process, using the first level as a second foundation. In the center of their supports was a hole exactly 24 inches in diameter. Engineers climbed ladders from the launch stand into the tank to the first level, ascended another ladder to the upper level, and could stand then to remove the styrofoam. Three engineers at a time worked inside the ten-foot-diameter fuel tank. They snipped out the styrofoam and the aluminum membrane, and passed them down through the entrance holes to men waiting below.

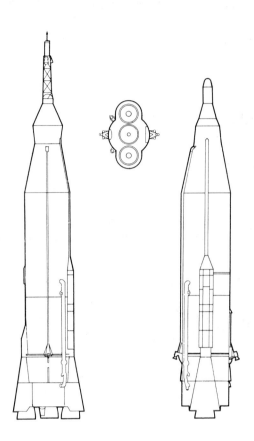

Four days after the crews first began to dismantle the sustainer engine the Atlas was again a complete unit. From start to finish the amazing task had been performed in just 96 hours!

General Dynamics/Astronautics had the great foresight to save all the wooden scaffolding that had been cut to the exact internal dimensions of the Atlas. And then, only days later, came the news that the same ruptured membrane had been found in Atlas 109-D, and that the styrofoam of Glenn's booster was soaked with kerosene.

The National Aeronautics and Space Administration went along with the recommendation of General Dynamics/Astronautics that the same procedures used for Ranger III be used for Mercury-Atlas 6. The decision was not easy to make. Ranger III

Tired, frustrated, but looking at the world with a quizzical grin, Glenn leaves the Mercury capsule on January 27, 1962, after spending five hours sweating out the countdown—which was scrubbed because of heavy clouds over Canaveral.

was a payload of instruments. John Glenn was a human being. If things had *not* worked out as they did . . . if the Atlas that carried Glenn into orbit had not performed with the sensational success that it demonstrated . . . if John Glenn had met disaster . . .

If any one of these things had happened—or any one of a dozen more that might have brought flaming catastrophe instead of a spectacular achievement—the men who made these hard, fast, knowledgeable decisions would have borne the guilt and the blame.

Of such things is history made. But in the wild, jubilant aftermath of Glenn's stirring flight through space, who thought of these engineers?

And who even remembers, today, that these dramatic, critical events went on day and night, without a stop for almost a week, so that an American astronaut might find his destiny in space?

Ol' Devil Weather

On February 14, I broadcast the following story throughout the network of Metropolitan Broadcasting (New York, Philadelphia, Cleveland, Kansas City, etc.):

"It's almost impossible to describe the feelings of people here in the Cape Canaveral area. This morning broke with a sky absolutely clear of clouds. The day is perfect for a launching, just as we had forecast for local conditions. But this is not the story downrange. . . . Shortly after midnight, the high waves and strong winds of the Atlantic Recovery Areas forced officials of the National Aeronautics and Space Administration to call off —for the ninth time—the flight of Astronaut John Glenn.

"The weather here at Canaveral will likely remain good for another two days at the most, and then we can expect some heavy cloud cover to start moving in. But even more important is downrange weather, and here the situation has Project Mercury officials ready to leap off buildings.

"Just east of Bermuda a storm area is still extremely active. It's the kind of sea condition, with a barometer needle dropping far down, that has veteran seamen nervous. Even more threatening is a new storm center that blew up this morning off Cape Hatteras and that is now thundering toward the Bermuda area. It should arrive there tomorrow morning with very strong winds and high, roaring seas . . . and will cover much of the area to the east and west of Bermuda. Still another storm is building up in the downrange recovery areas, and no matter how you look at it, downrange weather in the recovery areas for John Glenn is falling apart at the seams. . . ."

The history of the first American orbital flight around the world would be incomplete without mention of the cat-and-mouse game played for more than two months with the fickleness of nature. John Glenn and his great Atlas rocket were the principal players in the drama at Cape Canaveral, but they could never make a move without consideration for the weather.

There was, first, the problem of weather at Cape Canaveral. This began, finally, to cause many curious questions to be asked. Weather conditions under which many rockets and space vehicles had been launched with complete success were scorned for Mercury-Atlas 6.

Nothing stressed this problem more than the events that took place the morning of Saturday, January 27.

Everything was in readiness on this day. The Atlas, the capsule, tracking stations, recovery forces, the astronaut—they were all *Go*. In the weeks that had already passed, Glenn worked hard to keep himself in top condition—"honing the edge," as he called it. Each morning after breakfast he ran along the Canaveral beach for exercise. Then he went through what had been the normal routine at Hangar S and in the Mercury Control Building on the Cape. He went through medical examinations, spent hours of practice in the Mercury capsule simulator, studied star charts, and generally endured with a remarkable stolidity the problems of sweating out his own historic mission away from this planet.

Some newsmen described Glenn during the period of monumental tension buildups and crashing disappointments as "an island of disciplined calm." This appears to stretch the point, for certainly Glenn was as disappointed as anyone else at the delays, and the fact that he went through extensive, meaningful preparations each time only demanded more from him than anyone else. But Glenn is a combat fighter-pilot veteran. More important, he has extensive experience as a test pilot. And contrary to a belief widely held, most test flying is not exciting, but distressingly routine and dull. Test piloting has its moments—as the grave markers at the Air Force Flight Test Center in California attest grimly—but for the most part it insists upon men with extraordinary patience. Test pilots are selected carefully; the Mercury astronauts were selected from the ranks of the finest test pilots in the country. Glenn's reserve through the collective gnashing of teeth at Canaveral is not unusual; it would have been unusual had the situation been otherwise.

But the morning of January 27 may be regarded as about the ultimate test of his patience.

Everything was in the green for a shot. At two in the morning

Glenn awoke. He showered and ate a healthy breakfast of steak, eggs, toast, and coffee. General David M. Shoup, Marine Corps commandant, showed up unexpectedly at Hangar S for a surprise visit to his prize Marine. Then everything was business. Glenn donned his silvery, 20-pound spacesuit, went through careful pressure and equipment checks. Everything was fine, and Glenn left Hangar S for the brief van ride to Complex Fourteen on the Canaveral beachfront.

That morning was spectacular. The Atlas shone with a brilliant, glistening display of metal—created by batteries of giant floodlights that played on the rocket and across the red-and-white service gantry that loomed more than 12 stories above the Cape. It was a scene straight out of science fiction, and despite the continuing realization that it was all very real, it proved difficult to believe that all this . . . manned space flight . . . was really happening.

At 12 minutes past five o'clock, his helmet sealed tightly to his suit neckring, Glenn squeezed his way into the cramped confines of his spaceship. Then he began to go through his checklist of items for the capsule, the booster, communications, and the many other items necessary for a flight into space.

The entire world was ready and waiting for him. Glenn was scheduled for the earliest possible launch time of 7:30 a.m. But no matter what time of daylight he departed Cape Canaveral, it would be dark on the other side of the world. And in Perth, Australia, thousands of people were ready and waiting to remain awake all through the night. They were planning a special greeting for the American spaceman. As Glenn passed overhead, the entire city would come ablaze with lights for him to see as he gazed upon the darkened planet below him. It would be one of the grandest, most brilliant salutations of all time—measured at 10,000,000 watts.

The preparations completed, McDonnell technicians sealed the hatch onto the capsule with explosive bolts. The great gantry workstand rolled away, rumbling to its lock-and-hold stand 500 feet from the launch ring where the silvery Atlas and its small Mercury capsule waited out the rest of the countdown.

While we on the Cape watched directly—and 60,000,000 Americans watched on their television screens—for the minutes to drift toward the moment of firing, the countdown went through several minor crises. The technical bugs were quickly found and eliminated.

Inside the capsule, lying on his back and sealed in his suit, John Glenn, through a special telephone hookup, talked to his wife Anna at their home in Virginia.

That morning I thought that either a new concept of weather was being created or that NASA was simply going to ignore what was happening over Cape Canaveral. South and east of the Cape thick cumulus clouds appeared. Gray scud came whipping low over the horizon. High above the earth a mass of gray-white began to drift over Canaveral.

That morning I was broadcasting throughout the Metropolitan Network and to more than 20 nations in Europe, Africa, and South America (WRUL International). It must have been a strange broadcast. On the air I kept insisting that in view of the weather there could not possibly be a launching this morning. After the sun broke the horizon the sky became virtually opaque with clouds. Never did the clouds cover less than 85 per cent of the sky at any one time; most of the time the coverage above the Cape was almost complete.

Still the countdown went on. When the news came that NASA had directed the General Dynamics/Astronautics launch crew to start loxing the Atlas (fueling the liquid oxygen), a roar went up from the hundreds of newsmen at the Press Site on Canaveral. The excitement became a tangible thing.

My comment on the air was still "No go." A manned shot is not like a missile firing. To be absolutely certain that we will always know what happens with a manned firing—at least at this stage of the art of space flight—scientists *must* have what they call "optical access" to the rocket booster as it rises from the earth. Many times in the past an explosion that destroyed a missile remained an enigma from the data transmitted by radio to the ground. One Atlas, in fact, blew apart in the midst of a thick cloud deck. The Air Force never learned the cause of that missile loss.

The cat-and-mouse game of weather forecasting for Glenn's flight: on February 16, 1962 (reading left to right) *Dr. Hugh L. Dryden, Walter C. Williams, and Robert R. Gilruth* study the latest meteorological reports. Four days later Williams gave the Go signal for the spectacularly successful flight.

We couldn't afford this with Glenn's flight. In the event that there might be a failure, we had to have accurate film records of exactly what happened. Other men were to follow Glenn. A disaster with the Mercury-Atlas 6 mission could pinpoint the cause for the failure, and avoid that problem in the future.

So the sky over Canaveral had to be clear. As Colonel Powers explained the problem: "The determination of whether or not we will go on the basis of sky conditions will depend on the reports we get from the optical tracking devices. We get a periodic report about every thirty minutes during the countdown that tells us the reach—the estimated reach ability—of the optical tracking devices. They express this in percentage of the coverage that they think they can acquire. If the reports indicate 75- or 80-per-cent 'reach ability,' or 'coverage ability' on a given sky condition, we'll go. Bear in mind that this is just not in the Cape Canaveral area, as far as cloud coverage is concerned, because these optical instrumentation units are scattered up and down the beach.

"There have been many, many instances in the missile test program and space vehicle program where the optical record—the film record of a malfunction—has been much more revealing than the electronics and telemetry. You can instrument just so much in a vehicle. Then you have to look at the pictures to find out just what broke, what bent, or where the fire started."

And these considerations were just as valid the morning of January 27 at Cape Canaveral as they had always been in the past, which is why I insisted upon the "No go" report in my broadcast.

The count went to T-minus-20 minutes. Liquid oxygen inside the tank of the Atlas produced its familiar sheet of ice around the booster. White vapors drifted sluggishly about the base of the launch complex, and streams of gox (gaseous oxygen) plumed from the vent valves high on the rocket. Everybody got ready for the shot; the television networks and radio networks were all "live."

At T-minus-20 minutes—the time was ten minutes after nine—NASA officials scrubbed the mission. The sky conditions hadn't changed at all—sky obscuration was still at least 90 per cent.

The loxing process stopped; the oxidizer was dumped. Slowly the white ice sheets began to melt, and water ran down the curving flanks of the Atlas. Later, the massive gantry workstand began its ponderous movement back to the launch pad, to embrace the booster.

The technicians unbolted the hatch. John Glenn—tired, his red hair matted with perspiration—climbed out of his spacecraft. He had been in the capsule for more than five hours. His comment was terse: "Well, there'll be another day."

Downrange Weather

As I mentioned before, Cape Canaveral had a total of several weeks of perfect weather for launch conditions during the long wait for Glenn's flight—but it was impossible to commit the shot. The problem in these instances, entirely aside from any technical difficulties, was the status of weather at the downrange recovery areas.

There are four main recovery areas in which the weather must meet minimum requirements. When the flight begins, it might prove necessary to abort the mission during the latter stages of ascent, or even immediately after orbit is achieved. In the Atlantic, near the Canary Islands, was a long stretch of abort zones.

Glenn's flight was planned for either one, two, or three orbits, depending upon many factors, the most vital of which was the time of launch. On the first scheduled date of January 16, the earliest possible launch time was 7:30 a.m. If Glenn launched between 7:30 and 9:30 a.m., then, all things being equal in terms of spacecraft operation, the goal of the flight would be three orbits. A launch between 9:30 and 11:30 a.m. would call for a maximum of two orbits; launch after 11:30 a.m., with a cutoff time of 12:30 p.m., meant no more than one orbit.

The key to the time that might be spent in orbit was a period of three hours. The requirements for space flight demanded that at least three hours of daylight must be available for search and recovery operations from the moment the bell-shaped capsule dropped into the ocean.

"If we get involved in technical holds which put us beyond

about nine-thirty in the morning," explained Colonel Powers, "we might well go on a planned basis for two orbits. If we slip on beyond about 11 o'clock to about 12:30 we could well go on a planned one-orbit mission.

"These times are related to the requirements that we have for about three hours of daylight in each recovery zone. This would depend on the long-range weather forecast. If we get down into about ten o'clock and the weather people tell us there is going to be a real serious deterioration in weather for another week or ten days, we could well go on a pre-planned one-orbit mission. Again I remind you that this would give us 18 times more weightless flight experience than we got out of either the Shepard or Grissom flights."

The recovery area for one orbit was located in a zone at sea that is 500 miles east of Bermuda and 1,400 miles northeast of Cape Canaveral. Zone Number Two, for two orbits, lies 500 miles south of Bermuda and 1,000 miles due east of Canaveral. Zone Number Three is 800 miles southeast of Canaveral.

The weather conditions in these areas as concerned the *Go–No Go* decision depended upon varying factors, and only one man— Walter C. Williams, the launch operations director for Project Mercury—could give the word. Williams suffered what was unquestionably the most harassed position of anyone in the United States during the repeatedly delayed countdowns for Glenn's flight. The pressures building upon this man for the decision to *Go* were unbelievable. A lesser man might have yielded to the strong possibilities of good weather. But Williams divorced himself from everything but harsh realities. Unless the weather permitted no compromise with the safety of the astronaut who would make the flight, Atlas 109-D would never reach the point of igniting her mighty engines. Not until the gods, the weather, *and* Walt Williams all agreed could there be an uncompromised shot.

During the flights of Shepard and Grissom, the weather problems were enormously simplified. They were to soar down the Atlantic Missile Range only for some 300 miles. Weather was a problem only at the Cape during launch and for a few hours afterward in the one recovery zone.

We lacked experience early in 1961. The conditions for the suborbital flights demanded excellent sky weather at the Cape and downrange, and a sea condition of waves no higher than three feet with a mild wind.

After Shepard's flight in May of 1961, NASA scientists carried out extensive wind and wave tests with the Mercury capsule, and drew the conclusions that the spacecraft was much more seaworthy than had been believed. So Glenn's flight could get the green light even if the waves were higher than three feet. "NASA would rather stay away from specific figures," Colonel Powers explained, "because of the influence of other factors such as the distance between swells and wind conditions. We start getting concerned when seas are choppy and waves are five to six feet in height. When there are long swells, considerably greater heights can be tolerated."

But no matter how you looked at it, the observer on the scene at Cape Canaveral couldn't escape the impression that the pinnacle of American science had no choice but to play the loser's part in the continuing cat-and-mouse game with the weather.

The Rescuers

One of the more remarkable chapters in the story of the flight of John Glenn has never been fully told. Perhaps—and all concerned fervently hope so—it never will be fully told. This element of the space mission concerns a group of men about whom most Americans know surprisingly little.

These are the 63 pararescuemen of the Air Force's Air Rescue and Astronaut Recovery group who may mean the difference in life or death for an astronaut if his capsule plunges into the oceans of the world far from any assigned recovery area.

The jumpers of the pararescue teams include some of the toughest physical specimens of all the armed forces. They are trained to razor-sharp perfection in every field of the science of survival, and each man is also a skilled medical technician. Their lore of survival at sea, in the desert, in the mountains or swamps —anywhere, for that matter—has astounded veterans of global exploration trips. Added to this is their superb skill at precision parachuting into any type of terrain under almost any weather condition.

For John Glenn, they were his "ace in the hole."

Each man is an expert SCUBA technician (self-contained-underwater-breathing-apparatus)—in every sense of the word, a skilled frogman. Their stations for Mercury-Atlas 6 included alert duty aboard helicopters and planes in the area off Cape Canaveral in the event of a failure during the early launch, in the abort areas off the Canary Islands, and around the world. During the Glenn mission, the pararescue crews were standing by at stations around the planet in the event that Glenn was forced to leave his orbit because of an emergency, and descend as rapidly as possible. A mechanical failure, a meteor strike that

Landing field for the Mercury capsule . . . in the Atlantic, where a Marine Sikorsky helicopter retrieves the spacecraft from the ocean for a brief flight to nearby aircraft carrier.

damaged equipment—any one or several of a hundred different possibilities could have forced a mission abort.

But no matter where Glenn came down on the surface of the earth—liquid or solid—within 18 hours at the very most (this figure is ultra-cautious) the pararescuemen would have been on the scene. Probably even an isolated landing area would have meant contact with and rescue of Glenn within several hours of his descent.

If Glenn's capsule had "splashed" in mid-ocean, its location would first have been marked by the massive electronic computers of NASA. Planes would have been in the air and rushing to this position at the very first indication of trouble. The capsule itself would have been broadcasting a homing distress call through automatic systems. Dye markers would have spread brilliant colors on the surface of the sea. Smoke bombs would have been fired, also, to attract visual attention. Explosive charges would have exploded in the ocean far beneath the capsule as a homing source for ships equipped with sonar detection apparatus.

In his capsule and personal survival equipment, Glenn would have had little difficulty while waiting for recovery. The capsule itself was watertight and had floated for many hours at sea. Glenn's suit was watertight and would keep him afloat. In addition, the Mercury capsule survival system provides for the astronaut a raft made of mylar plastic and colored international orange, a desalting kit, shark repellent, dye markers, a first-aid kit, a signal mirror, distress signals, a portable radio, rations, matches, drugs, a whistle, and other items—more than enough to sustain him for any time he may spend at sea before he is reached by his rescue teams.

The pararescue crews, flying in four-engine transports, have had extensive experience at this work. They have recovered capsules from our Discoverer satellites in mid-ocean under conditions that sometimes were "hazardous."

In the event of a mid-ocean landing by a manned capsule, the pararescue plane is directed to make a pass over the astronaut at a thousand feet. First one man goes out (the jumpers

There may not always be help around after impacting with the ocean. . . .
Scott Carpenter practices "egress training" from the Mercury capsule in
a giant water tank.

have hit the water consistently under high wind conditions at
sea within 20 or less yards of their objective). As he drifts down,
the airplane turns and makes a second pass—and another man
goes out and, shortly after, a third man hits the silk.

As the men descend beneath their parachutes (they are wearing full SCUBA equipment), they immediately jettison their reserve chutes. Next they deploy a one-man life raft, extend it by a
lanyard, and inflate the raft. A first-aid kit also extends far below
the jumper, attached to a lanyard. The jumper then pulls safety
clips and as his feet touch the water he jettisons his main parachute canopy.

In the water the pararescue man is as much at home as he
is on land. He remains on the surface momentarily to check his
equipment. Then he takes a compass bearing on the capsule
and goes below the water surface, swimming underwater and
towing the inflated one-man raft behind him.

As the rescue team swims toward the capsule, the transport

roars overhead—and out comes another heavy package to drift seaward by parachute. This is a special flotation belt. The rescue team quickly attach the belt to the bottom of the capsule, about its base. This gives the capsule added buoyancy, greatly improves its steadiness in the water, and assures that the side hatch will remain above the waterline.

Back comes the airplane. The jumpmaster in the transport releases a heavy MA-1 Kit—a specially constructed sea-survival kit that contains two 20-man life rafts, three survival bundles of food, blankets, medical supplies, radios, and other equipment. The rafts are inflated, the equipment brought aboard. If any further help is needed, the jumpmaster also goes out of the airplane.

With the large rafts out, the survival group then have two 20-man rafts and three one-man rafts, plus the astronaut's own one-man raft, and the flotation-stabilized capsule as well. In past capsule-retrieving operations with the Discoverer satellite program, the pararescue men have, when necessary, remained overnight at sea, waiting for flying boats or ships to come to the scene.

They've practiced extensively with models of the Mercury capsule, and their accuracy and success have been nothing less than phenomenal.

John Glenn didn't need their services—and they couldn't be happier about that fact. But Scott Carpenter did need their services and the emergency rescue system was proved out brilliantly.

Other astronauts are following Carpenter. Many flights will be made, and it's comforting to know that the pararescue teams will always be available for any emergency situation.

And who knows? One day they might find themselves airborne and on their way to rescue a Russian spaceman—down at sea, "somewhere in the world."

Shadow of the New Age

The greater majority of events and activities that produced the orbital flight of Astronaut John Glenn went unseen by the public eye, and it would be impossible within these pages to describe even briefly the full spectrum of the operations involved. But one other moment out of the vast stirring around the world deserves our attention. In the recovery force on January 26 that cruised the Atlantic far from Cape Canaveral was the aircraft carrier USS *Enterprise*. Aboard this warship was Chet Di Mauro of Associated Press, a newsman selected to represent the nation's press through the NASA Project Mercury Press Pool. Di Mauro captured with feeling a moment far at sea:

> A feeling of historic destiny pervades the USS *Enterprise* today—the second ship in line to recover the nation's first man to orbit earth.
>
> The *Enterprise*, whose name was first etched on wooden planks . . . in the 1700's, today cast its nuclear-powered silhouette on Atlantic water. The first-born of man's plunge into the ships of the future was waiting for word for changes of plans to launch Astronaut John Glenn, Jr., into a planned three-orbit journey around earth.
>
> The world's biggest vessel was maneuvering into a predetermined recovery position . . . southeast of Bermuda. Its recovery team was ready and well trained to move into action should Glenn's Mercury capsule be triggered back to earth after two orbits.
>
> To observers on board, the very design and space-age feel of the island-ship seems to be the perfect predestined setting for the recovery of the bell-shaped capsule returning from an orbital flight through space.
>
> The feeling is inescapable when walking on the seemingly endless flight deck on a moonlit night. When one casts an unbelieving eye on the carrier's superstructure, which appears to be jutting from the very sea like a monstrous squid, it seems that this is the ship's periscope taking a reading of the earth itself. . . .

Scuba divers of Air Force pararescue teams practice new emergency recovery techniques; that's Alan Shepard emerging from the top of the Mercury capsule.

II : *Prelude to a Distant Day*

THE FIVE WEEKS before the final moment of zero in the launch countdown for John Glenn was a period amply described to the entire United States. The frustrations and anxieties arising from the repeated countdown holds, delays, scrubs, and postponements became a wearying pattern familiar to all America. From schoolchildren to aged veterans, Americans pursued eagerly every scrap of news from Cape Canaveral. Even a weather announcement affecting the schedule generated sufficient interest to justify news bulletins.

During this time the great Atlas booster remained standing on Complex Fourteen. Suspicion began to grow among Canaveral veterans that we might have a repetition of the Mercury-Atlas 2 program on our hands. The shudders that swept through the groups discussing this possibility were actually visible.

The Atlas booster for Mercury-Atlas 2 stood on its launch pad for *six months.*

Throughout the United States, the waiting for Glenn's orbital flight became a daily routine of life. People accepted the delays, shrugged their shoulders, and decided that if John Glenn could sweat it out, so could they. In the meantime, just about everything else at Cape Canaveral seemed to grind to a halt.

Many people truly believed our entire space program was at a standstill—but this was patently not true. Mercury-Atlas 6 was a vital shot in our program, but it was, after all, only one of many other space projects simultaneously under way. And there were military launchings as well to be carried out.

Two Pershing missiles boomed skyward during the five weeks preceding Glenn's historic space mission. The Pershing is a solid-propellant missile of two stages. It is compact, powerful, and an extraordinarily deadly battlefield weapon. At the Cape, Pershing was going through its final development phase, and the crews were launching their rockets under simulated field conditions.

Unfortunately, this wasn't the best phase of the Pershing development program, which, over-all, was phenomenally successful. The holds in the Pershing countdowns were unprecedented, but nevertheless we were there on those occasions when the Army missiles briefly turned night into day. One Pershing shot created a strange rippling streak of yellow light that burned a needlelike path through low, misty clouds—and then abruptly vanished in the darkness, committed to its ballistic arc that would end in a simulated target far from the Cape's beaches.

The Air Force launched several Mace missiles, a throwback to the "old days" of robot weapons—"old days" that went back in time less than a decade. Mace is a pilotless, jet engine-powered bomber—a 700-mile-per-hour winged robot that seems painfully slow in its performance and archaic in its lines despite its sleek nose and sweptback wings. It doesn't fly very high and it can't fly even at the speed of sound—factors that apparently made the Mace an anachronism at Cape Canaveral, where a man was waiting to hurtle around the planet at 18,000 miles per hour.

But the Mercury capsule in which John Glenn would sail the seas of space—close to its shores—was a scientific gadget. Despite its complexity and its staggering cost, it was a vehicle designed to orbit a man, keep him alive in space, and return him safely to earth. It performed no specific mission, served no purpose other than that of seeking out information for which we were prepared to pay dearly—perhaps even at the cost of a man's life.

By contrast, the old, slow, obsolescent Mace, ignoring its short-comings, exists as a deadly weapon. Despite its *apparent* weaknesses the Mace is a killer of armies and of cities. In its pointed nose it can hold a heavy, powerful bomb with an explosive force measured in the millions of tons of TNT. Mace does not plunge through the heavens in the type of performance we have come to expect of the age of space. There is no spectacular vertical launch for Mace.

The missile fired at Cape Canaveral thunders along a gentle angle from the ground into the air—from deep within the concrete bowels of a steel-reinforced concrete-readiness shelter. Watching a Mace launch, especially from a close distance, is a shattering experience. The jet engine shrieks at full speed with an ear-piercing noise for several minutes before the countdown reaches zero. Then a giant booster bottle—a thick, long, solid-propellant rocket—explodes into a frenzied motion of howling fire and the sound of a dozen volcanoes all erupting in a devastating chorus. The sound fills the launch shelter and then, almost as if to flee from itself, roars hoarsely at the world as it bursts free.

Amidst all this, rammed forward by the lashing red and yellow fire of the booster rocket, rushes the Mace. It leaps from nowhere into sight, shoved inexorably by the flaming power of the booster rocket in its steady climb, accelerating steadily. Abruptly the flame gasps, curls in upon itself. Displaying short, flickering yellow fire tongues, the booster is unceremoniously jettisoned by the Mace. Now the missile is moving fast enough for its own wings to grasp lift from the air, for the jet engine to sustain the high subsonic flight.

The Mace does not climb high. Instead, the sweptwing weapon remains low. And down the Atlantic Missile Range it races, dodging and twisting, turning, banking and sliding through the sky in a fantastic simulated flight through the rugged terrain of an enemy's land. The fact that Mace can perform this miraculous electronic feat in darkness, in rain or in snow, at any time of day or night, and never move more than a few feet above the highest ground obstacle as it probes and darts along under the guidance of its mindless robot brain—the fact that Mace can do all these things—makes the slow, winged jet creature a weapon of terrible effectiveness.

But the eyes of the world were on a silvery giant numbered 109-D, and thoughts were about a man named Glenn. Most papers never carried a line about the launchings of Mace, nor did reporters note that many of these winged weapons are on immediate-launch alert status on several continents and islands.

One of the paradoxes of the space age is that many of the weapons that reach out into the vacuum of space before they plunge back into the atmosphere receive the flaming impetus for their flights from deep *within* the earth. In the five-week period prior to Glenn's space mission, two lethal missiles burst skyward in accelerated-period tests of their battle capabilities.

One of these was Polaris—stubby, with two solid-propellant stages, and easily the most deceiving bludgeon of the missile era. Much smaller than most ballistic rockets, Polaris—if ever it is needed in war—will herald its birth in combat with a sudden gush of water from mid-ocean. Carried in the bowels of a nuclear-driven submarine, and popping like a monstrous cork to the surface, Polaris is ejected from below the sea by a charge of compressed air. It gains its first spark of life only after its motor nozzles are well clear of the water. No stately performance here —only a savage stream of fire, and a rising line of white smoke to mark the course of Polaris rushing toward space. Then, a second gleam of flame, high up—Stage II coming into pyrotechnic life.

Unfortunately, the Polaris launched during the "long wait" functioned well only during the brief life of the first-stage boost section. Something in the upper stage failed; a preplanned course of straight and true flight became instead a violent, tumbling motion that at Cape Canaveral is the aerial signature of failure.

To the immense satisfaction of project engineers and the military planners of the nation—and also to all of us who watched the scene—the test of the Minuteman intercontinental ballistic missile was as perfect a success as could be achieved. Minuteman is in a class all to itself—three solid-propellant rocket stages packaged into a true powerhouse of flaming energy. One day, when the Minuteman program is complete, 800 of these city-killers will be buried deep underground in the northern and northwestern sections of America—ICBMs vanished beneath the earth in deep vertical silos.

The firings at Cape Canaveral are prelude to those distant days

which, if civilization is to escape a savage mauling, we hope
will never come.

You look at an empty space across Cape Canaveral for Minuteman; from a distance you are unable to see even the vacant circle
in the earth deep within which Minuteman is poised. The countdown crackles over the loudspeakers on the Cape—hesitating for
deliberate, "built-in" holds during the last seconds—and finally
stops at the cry of zero.

No missile appears. Instead, a tremendous gash of searing red
flame erupts upward from the ground, an incredible tongue of
fire—the exhaust of Minuteman's first stage, already bent and
vented to the surface. Simultaneously with the abrupt appearance of the flame that bursts high above Canaveral there is a
perfect white smoke ring, a circle that pushes up from the Cape
—a jest contrasting with the deadly purpose of the firing. Things
happen so quickly they seem impossible. Without notice, in the
midst of the enormous lance of fire there appears Minuteman,
flames streaming back from the missile. For an instant it seems
to hang above the ground, but in reality it is accelerating at a
furious pace. Thick white smoke follows the blaze in the skies;
the missile programs quickly away from the horizontal and soon
the flame begins to disappear behind the smoke.

On that clear day at the Cape and with excellent visibility, I
watched through binoculars as the first stage winked out and
the second stage stabbed at the air with its own fire as it began
to rush away. The spent first stage tumbled in a falling-leaf
pattern from the high skies, a strangely graceful sign of energy
exhausted, surrounded by a thin double-lined contrail of white,
while much higher and farther along the range, Stage III had
already reached its speed of 15,000 miles per hour.

During the next several minutes, the dummy warhead reached
out into vacuum, followed the inexorable path of its course as
dictated by centrifugal force, and returned to impact on target.
In that brief time a simulated nuclear warhead had already been
in space, returned, and "splashed" into its impact area some
4,000 miles away.

Although we waited during those five weeks prior to Glenn's shot to watch Atlas 109-D thunder into the sky, we watched two other Atlas firings—one as a space booster, the other in its original form as the ICBM.

The latter was the firing of the last Atlas-E missile from Cape Canaveral as a prototype weapon. During a long afternoon countdown under a deep blue sky, delayed several times by holds, the Air Force prepared to take a major step forward in the deployment of its giant robot weapons. Lox plumes boiled furiously from the vent valves of the missile, and at the cry of zero in the count the ice-shrouded rocket pushed its way from the earth.

Atlas E burned with an unusually brilliant, golden light. Her thunder crashed down onto the Cape, carried by an easterly wind that often can double the volume of the rocket sound as heard by the Cape observer. Glenn's 109-D booster would lift him up from the earth with great power, but the E-model we watched on that afternoon carried a brace of engines much more powerful than those to be used in the impending space flight.

Atlas E howled her way into the heavens, arced over in a curving climb, and vanished from sight. Less than 30 minutes later the word came in. The warhead had plunged from the sky 5,000 miles away and with "fantastic accuracy" ripped into the impact zone's center.

The other Atlas received much greater attention, for atop this D-model booster rested an upper stage called Agena B. And within the white, bulbous plastic nose cone of the Agena B rested an electronic miracle—Ranger III. This was the ninth lunar probe that our country was to fire at the moon. We hoped fervently we would witness a launching that would culminate finally in success.

Ever since the early morning of August 17, 1958, I had watched our lunar probes flame their way upward from the sands of Canaveral. Eight times we tried for the moon, and eight times we had failed. The Russians whipped a giant package only 3,200 miles from the lunar surface in a marvelously accurate *Lunik I* shot. Their *Lunik II* crashed at more than two miles per second into the center of the moon—270 miles from dead center, in fact, in a flight that was off its schedule by only 84 seconds. It was a flight the usually staid astronomers of England (who tracked the probe) described as "fabulous," "amazing," and with "utterly fantastic precision in guidance." *Lunik III* sailed about the moon, taking and developing pictures of its far side, and then sent these back to the earth.

All this in *1959*.

But this was 1962, and hopes ran high that finally the United States would make it. The Atlas-D booster flung back its golden fireball. Trailing the long plumes of thin violet flames, with shock diamonds barely visible to the eye, Ranger III departed the earth in what was one of the most beautiful Atlas launches ever made. And a good omen appeared in the heavens. As the broad swath of the white contrail appeared in the stratosphere, the horizontal winds shredded the trail into an enormous, perfect, stratospheric 3—an omen of success, we hoped.

But we were wrong, and once again a failure registered in the record books. The intricate, expensive ($6,000,000) payload of 675 pounds sailed ahead of the moon in its orbit, missing that lifeless hulk of a world by about 22,000 miles. Its sensitive television camera worked, but not its radar screens, and the pictures taken by Ranger III sprayed uselessly into space. The probe disappeared into the deeps of the solar system to take up an orbit about the sun.

Failure though Ranger III was, there arose from the firing of this probe—and that of Atlas E—a heartening regard to the future when Glenn's own mission would begin. Both Atlas vehicles functioned beautifully; the Atlas that boosted Ranger III "overspeeded" slightly, but even this fault would have brought success to Glenn's long-delayed flight. Solace was welcome at this point, even as a promise for a third consecutive firing in which the Atlas motors burned perfectly.

The US Navy—using an Air Force Thor-Ablestar booster—attempted early one morning to launch a "quintuplet satellite system." With one rocket firing the Navy wanted to fling five small scientific satellites into orbit. The satellites clustered about a rigging atop the third stage like a glittering Christmas tree. Although the satellites individually did not amount to anything impressive in weight, their equipment was vital for a series of scientific experiments in space. And judging from the eager words of the Navy personnel present—and an elaborate press release handed out on the basis of "Hold until successful launch before release"—the Navy would make great news copy with their five satellites orbited in a single shot.

They failed to achieve the news column space they desired, but this was one time that the failure of the scientific goals was almost overshadowed by the strange and deep beauty of the launching.

The night of the firing a heavy mist settled over the Cape Canaveral area. On the Cape itself, as we arrived, the mist hung heavily to the surface for 50 feet above the ground, so thick that we couldn't see the brilliant lights along Atlas and Titan Row.

The Cape was strangely quiet, its morning sounds muffled by the blankets of mist. Far ahead of where we stood on a wooden platform high above the ground, searchlights suddenly broke the quiet gloom. But this morning there were no brilliant beams stabbing the skies. The mist absorbed the light, sucking it inward as a dry sponge grasps eagerly at moisture.

Only the very top of the space rocket was visible. Through powerful rangefinders I studied the protective nose cone as it seemed to try to reach higher above the swirling mists. Every now and then a gap appeared in the silent ghosts of fog, and a flank of the white rocket appeared briefly before being again embraced.

In a perfect countdown without a delay the count reached zero and the powerful booster motor ignited. For seconds there came not a sound. Neither did there appear the glaring splash of fire across Pad 17A that I had seen there so many times in the past. A golden hue diffused the mists. Then she rose from the launch ring, bringing the source of the golden flame nearer the upper level of the ground fog. In that instant the light flashed swiftly across the entire Canaveral beach area before us—a light of sparkling gold that seemed to set all of Cape Canaveral briefly aflame.

At almost the same moment the thunder rolled down upon us. The events happened swiftly, parts of their activity came concurrently, and the whole of the picture before us was a marvelous fabric of golden light and thunder . . . and the booster crashing upward into the night skies. High, high above again-darkened Cape Canaveral she went. Then, burnout—and Stage II splashed multi-colored balls of fire back against the rejected Thor booster. The second stage burned fiercely as it reached deeper into space.

At that second I knew she would never reach her goal of orbit. I have seen many Thor boosters and the upper stages fire at night, and on this morning the flame was not certain or true or even clean. The fire was speckled and splotched, a deeper and unhealthier red than normal. The burning was "imperfect."

Somewhere, thousands of miles away, the five satellites returned to earth to crash uselessly into the ocean.

There remained one other firing to recall to mind—a launch, shortly after darkness folded over Canaveral, that was the most beautiful and startling sight I have ever seen in 12 years at this coastal gateway to space.

On January 29, the Air Force planned an early-afternoon flight test of its last Titan I ICBM—a 98-foot, two-stage giant that was shortly to be declared operational. Forty-six Titans had been fired to date from Cape Canaveral in a development program highlighted by a remarkable ratio of successes to failures for an experimental rocket. By this date Titan I was no longer merely a test vehicle for the weapon series; inside the bulky weapon there was mounted an advanced type of guidance system. This was a "pushbutton" guidance designed for use with Titan II, an even heavier and more powerful giant that would soon begin tests. With the firing of the last Titan I, however, it would be possible to gain a major time advantage in flying Titan II.

Through the afternoon the countdown went through repeated delays and holds. The hours passed slowly, and still the technical delays and problems continued to plague the important shot. By the time the count resumed, the sun vanished below the horizon. In the final twilight the brilliant searchlights suddenly came on.

It was a breathtaking sight. I stood at a roadblock barely 2,000 feet from the giant missile. The lights flashed on the gleaming ice shrouding the Titan's fuel tanks. She loomed big and powerful, casting off streamers of bluish-white gox (gaseous oxygen). I could barely hear the shrill scream of the liquid-oxygen plumbing—a shrieking chorus of supercold metal set to its outlandish cry by the effects of temperature and wind.

Darkness swelled over the land, and the first stars came out clearly. The count continued—a "live one this time."

The searchlights winked out almost as if darkness had stamped out the beams. The squawk box along the roadside chanted the count. All about me were dozens of vehicles—fire trucks, crash crews, ambulances, wreckers, and other members of the ground team who support every firing at the Cape. Their crews also watched, and in the final seconds we took one last look around for a vehicle—under which we would scramble hastily if that great missile should explode during launch. This close to the giant we could be showered with the shrapnel-like debris of any such blast.

Through binoculars I watched the vapor plumes disappear, that final visible sign of impending zero, when the lox tanks are sealed and fully pressurized. I put down the glasses. This close they would be worthless.

Thirty-one minutes past six o'clock the launching pad exploded in a glorious burst of golden fire. Light flashed in all directions as the Titan broke free of gravity and began her ride away from earth. Then it was impossible to see anything but light—savage, intolerable golden light from the twin chambers. Two thousand feet distant? Impossible! They seemed to be right down the road, only bare yards away, pouring forth light so intense that it bleached the blackness out of the night.

The golden fireball lifted above the earth to announce the sound. For a second, no more, the sound could be distinguished. Then it struck with all its fury, and it seemed that a great knife of sound split the sky asunder. It was no longer sound, but the

Titan I lifts in a blaze of golden fire from Cape Canaveral.

mouth of a volcano erupting shock waves. You no longer heard the sound; it punched at you and embraced the body and everything seemed to vibrate just a bit in resonance with the cry of the *thing*. For Titan herself could no longer be seen, the white outline of the curving steel flanks hidden by the golden fire that demanded full attention. Even as I turned to look up, to follow the ascent, I still saw the faint outlines of that original blazing fireball, as though I were seeing a double image.

The thunder shook off its harsh overtones; the waves of sound receded to a cry that was familiar—the acetylene-torchlike howl of a giant clawing its path away from the gravity of earth.

She rose, faster and faster, accelerating rapidly. The flame revealed thin hollow tubes of fire within which shock diamonds paraded in an endless stream. I placed the rangefinders to my eyes; the miles shrunk magically and I was seeing the wonder— close up—of Titan racing away. She bent in her flight, leaning into the southeast toward the course that would bring the warhead far down the range.

The yellow became deep red and—suddenly—Titan was free of darkness. It was still early night. The line of shadow cast by the earth stretched far over our heads, but Titan was rushing from night back into daylight. Abruptly, flinging herself out of the night, the long rocket and her fire trail were struck by the sun already well disappeared beyond the horizon. First the flame became a blood color, then a rich orange with increasing height. Where Titan was, a man could no longer breathe; the giant plunged into the lower edges of space itself.

And then began what one meteorologist in justifiable wonder called *Aurora Titanalis*. Alvin B. Webb, my good friend from United Press International, described what was happening as "one of the most awesome and beautiful sights of the space age."

Behind the flame appeared the contrail—the long, wide swath of condensation. For a moment it was dark; struck by the sun's rays, it became a multicolored streak rising higher and higher above the earth.

Titan exhausted the fuel of her first stage. Well out into near vacuum, the two blazing combustion chambers shut down. There

came a moment without fire, but it was possible still to see the
deep red glow of the chambers. Timers clicked within the second stage, ignition began in space, and the upper-stage engine
burst into life.

And there began 600 seconds of sorcery.

In the silence of space a glistening halo appeared around the
burning upper stage. Ionized gases from the accelerating rocket
rushed about in all directions, causing the halo to spread with
tremendous speed. Normally it is invisible to the eye, but at this
moment, hundreds of miles high, it absorbed the full illumination of the sun—while we were in darkness.

The halo spread wider and wider, a huge pulsating globe that
became a pale green in color, and then began to reveal glittering
spots of pink and deep purple. About me on the Cape, even the
road guards, who have seen literally hundreds of rockets fire
from Canaveral, gasped in startled admiration as the teardrop
expanded rapidly until it was more than 100 miles wide.

In the midst of the intensely glowing gases in space, deepen-
ing steadily in greenish hue, lights appeared and began to move.
The second stage of Titan burned fiercely, but through the
plasma teardrop the color was not the familiar red or yellow
or orange; instead, it was a white-green with pulsating sapphire
points. As it rushed higher and faster with every passing second,
it produced its own bulging gaseous envelope, a growing circle
within the much vaster teardrop.

Soon we watched the light coming back at us in the form of
whorls and eddies, great glittering spirals, one after the other,
a plasma whirlpool in the heavens far above the upper edges of
the planet's atmosphere. The Titan engine kept blazing, pushing
the upper stage higher and higher.

Then, to the right and below this light, appeared a single blazing jewel, a hard, white-green light not from Titan. This was
the planet Venus, gleaming through the swirling kaleidoscope
of green.

Still another light appeared! Higher than the rest, it seemed,
but this was an optical illusion. It was the empty first stage of
Titan, tumbling end over end from space, dropping back into the

atmosphere. Friction tore at the metal skin; the steel glowed, then began to burn, and the twisting, tumbling fall of the flaming rocket added an orange-purple sheen to the sight before us. Without the rangefinders, the sight was incredibly huge. The teardrop had stretched, wider and longer, and now it became an enormous white balloon of wispy substance tinged with the green hue of the swirling eddies.

Through the rangefinders, however, the colors leaped into prominence. The pulsating rocket motor kept the strange whirlpool of space spinning madly, flinging its glittering ribbons in all directions until, in the minutes that passed, we were seeing several layers of whorls, all moving, all clashing and passing into and through one another. It was the most fantastic, beautiful sight I have ever seen.

The first stage appeared to be higher than both the still-burning upper stage and Venus because of the earth's curvature. The upper stage was bending far over in its flight, beginning to follow the arc of the planet. But the first stage had soared up and over, and was now coming down, much closer to us. And so it *seemed* to be higher—just as a person watching a distant airplane as he stands beneath a tree "sees" the airplane as moving beneath its branches, when the airplane may be miles above the earth.

For perhaps ten minutes the celestial display remained for us to see. Then, slowly, the lights began to disappear. Soon only the gleam of Venus remained to pierce sharply the dissipating teardrop in the heavens.

It was a display for millions of people to see. From Miami into the Carolinas people rushed to the streets to stare open-mouthed at the sky. Thousands of telephone calls flooded police switchboards along the eastern coast and well inland as people tried to identify the source of the unprecedented glistening teardrop with its spinning whorls and spirals.

Aurora Titanalis was perhaps an omen—and a welcome one—of the morrow. Several days before, a stranger had come to Cape Canaveral, disgorged from the capacious belly of a huge transport plane. Trucks carried their precious cargo to the Cape and rumbled gingerly into a sprawling industrial hangar where technicians and engineers waited to receive their new charge.

This was the first Titan II, the most powerful missile weapon ever devised by the United States. No liquid oxygen would ever pour into her tanks; no kerosene would be stored within the curving metal walls. Titan II carried within her metal tanks a hypergolic fuel—a fuel that could be stored for long periods of time, a fuel that was self-igniting. To launch Titan II, the fuel would be rammed through lines, flung past opened valves, to meet in the combustion chambers. Upon contact the streams would react with flaming violence, and Titan II would lift from the earth.

The new Titan was a weapon. She would carry an enormous warhead, measured not in megatons, but in tens of megatons of thermonuclear energy. From her first-stage engines there would stream 430,000 pounds thrust—65,000 pounds thrust greater than that generated by Atlas to send Astronaut Glenn into space. But this is not all—the second stage would burst into life with 100,-000 pounds thrust from its own engine.

Titan II was a weapon, but men on Cape Canaveral looked at her powerful lines with something else in their minds.

She was also the booster for Gemini—the two-man space capsule that would be larger, bulkier, twice as heavy as the Mercury spacecraft. With Titan II we would make our first multiman flights, hopefully in 1963, perhaps more realistically early the year following. The astronauts of Gemini would open a new page, a day once very distant, now suddenly much closer. For Gemini, the two-man orbital capsule, would rendezvous with Agena spacecraft in orbit about the earth. Gemini would experiment with the rendezvous technique in space, so that when the three-man lunar spaceship Apollo was ready for flight in 1965–67, we might be able to save precious months, perhaps even a year, in reaching the surface of the moon.

Still more men looked at Titan II and saw—Titan III. The hulking form of the new booster would change its external shape. Engineers had designed great solid-propellant rockets, each ten feet in diameter, to be strapped to each side of Titan II. In this fashion 1,000,000 pounds thrust would pull the booster off the ground and fling it into the skies for the Titan II motors to blaze.

And atop this new space tug would be another, different spaceship—a 15,000-pound Dyna-Soar, a manned vehicle with wings, to rush through space and return to the earth in the form of a true manned vehicle—under the control and guidance of its pilot—to land as an airplane on the surface of the earth.

These are all parts of the story to be told later in this book. But of one thing I am certain: when the day comes that I stand on Cape Canaveral and watch the Gemini ships thunder into space . . . when I watch the Apollo vehicles leave for another world 240,000 miles across space . . . none of them will surpass the deep beauty of that sight in the early evening of January 29, 1962, when the last of the Titan I's blazed her final message in—truly—the heavens above earth.

III : *The Vast Orchestration*

THE SPACE MISSION of one man calls for the intricately co-ordinated work of tens of thousands of men.

The preparations for flight into orbit from Cape Canaveral demand extensive preparations around the surface of the entire planet.

The one man who has the *least* to do during the final hours of any countdown is the man . . . who will leave behind him the earth.

The countdown is a vast orchestration, demanding the movement of great forces of men and machines, the manipulation of electrons and of ponderous vessels at sea. It must be co-ordinated along a single "time hack"; for in a countdown, day and night in the usual sense of the word are discarded, and everyone functions according to Greenwich Mean Time as measured on one line that slices the globe through England. This is *Zulu Time*, and all time references for the flight operate on the basis of Zulu. The integration of many activities is precise beyond our comprehension. A Time Signal Generator deep within the Central Control Building of Cape Canaveral (more specifically, the Cape Canaveral Missile Test Annex of the Air Force Missile Test Center) sends out pulses for co-ordination by many installations and many men—the pulses for the most delicate instruments are measured down to one millionth of a second; for the "cruder" instruments, down to one thousandth of a second.

First—a point that quickly becomes forgotten in the deep emotional current that runs through the impending mission of Glenn.

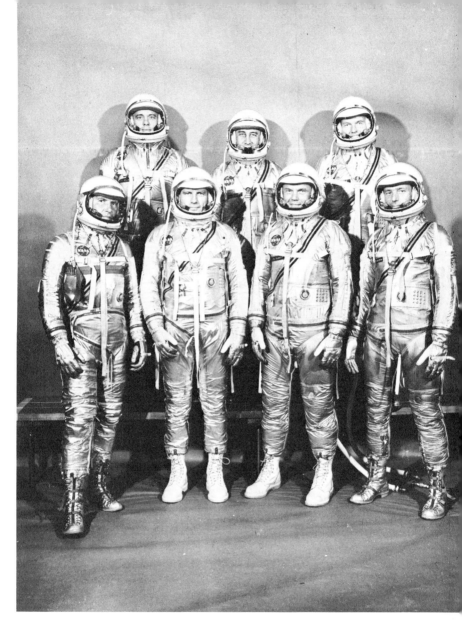

Astronauts all . . . Front row, left to right: *Walter M. Schirra, Jr., Donald K. Slayton, John H. Glenn, Jr., and M. Scott Carpenter.* Back row, left to right: *Alan B. Shepard, Jr., Virgil I. Grissom, and Leroy Gordon Cooper, Jr. Each man is a qualified engineer, test pilot, and astronaut.*

Why? Why is he making this flight? What is the purpose of his hazardous plunge into a fall about the planet, and even more dangerous return through the blazing reefs of friction back to safety?

Stripped of its technical jargon and removed of its political-propaganda overtones, the *why* of the mission is specific and meaningful.

The intrinsic purpose of this first American manned orbital flight is to observe and to *evaluate both the man and the spacecraft,* to see how they function during the launch, the climb, the injection into orbit. To see how well Man—in this instance John Glenn—can operate in the environment of space. To see how well he can endure and possibly even take advantage of his exposure to sustained zero gravity (weightlessness). To observe and evaluate his condition during and after exposure to hard cosmic radiation, to the many powerful forces of gravity in acceleration and deceleration during the ascent and re-entry. To allow John Glenn as our first astronaut in orbit to evaluate the systems and the capabilities of the spacecraft, the booster vehicle, and all other systems involved with the mission.

Mercury-Atlas is the springboard for all future manned space-flight operations of the United States. What it teaches us becomes the baseline of reference for everything else we do with men beyond the planet earth.

Thus as essential a part of this mission as any other is the need to control, observe, record, decode, and evaluate *everything* that occurs during every moment of the mission. And the heart of this operation for Glenn's space flight is the Project Mercury Control Center on Cape Canaveral. Here a large team of skilled technicians carries out the requirements of world-wide constant observation and control.

Throughout the flight—indeed, before it ever begins—it is necessary that physiological data on the man, environmental data inside the capsule, and engineering data on the capsule and its flight must be acquired, displayed instantly, and also recorded at the Mercury Control Center. The acquisition and use of this data permit the technical and control staff to operate as the central world operations control point throughout the mission.

Technical data—the parameters of performance—are fed to the Control Center from the capsule by telemetry (radio transmission of electronically coded information). As the capsule orbits the earth, information is fed to the Control Center from the 18 world-wide data stations located strategically along the orbital path of the spacecraft. A key function for information is also carried out by the Goddard Space Flight Center in Maryland, where dual IBM 7090 electronic computers receive, digest, compute, and spit forth information on a "real time" basis—i.e., virtually just as quickly as things happen, and also on a constant prediction of what *will* happen at any given moment (we'll be back later to Goddard).

The Operations Room is where there are made the hard-and-fast decisions of Glenn's flight (which is to become the scene of a taut and grim drama). It is 50 by 60 feet, a sprawling enclosure where men and electronics merge in a strange and wonderful team. The operations director, who sits at the center of the room toward the rear, is flanked on his right by the launch facility director and on his left by the recovery operations director. In front of the operations director (Walter C. Williams) is the flight director (C. C. Kraft), and he in turn is flanked by the network status monitor and the launch vehicle telemetry monitor.

The third tier—moving from the rear of the room forward—in front of the flight director includes the support control coordinator, flight surgeon, capsule environment monitor, capsule communicator, and capsule systems monitor.

Along the right wall of the room are the flight dynamics officer and the retrofire controller; before them is a display of four flight recorders. Recorder No. 1, states the official NASA explanation, "plots the launch path as *gamma* (inertial flight path angle) versus velocity ratio, and the orbital path as altitude above spherical earth versus velocity.

"Recorder No. 2 plots the launch path as cross range deviation and altitude versus range, and the orbital path as semimajor axis deviation and altitude versus ground elapsed time.

"Recorder No. 3 plots insertion velocity and longitudinal ac-

All personnel man their console stations in Mercury Control during a simulated space mission. Map shows World Tracking Network.

celeration versus elapsed time and yaw error and insertion altitude versus time-to-go-to-sustainer-engine cutoff, and the orbit as earth-fixed longitude of perigee, and eccentricity versus elapsed time.

"Recorder No. 4 plots a chart of the launch recovery area. One pen plots the landing point if the retrorockets are fired immediately before tower separation and also the landing point if the retrorockets are fired in 30 seconds. The second pen plots the landing point for a time of retrofire for maximum delay when the capsule reaches a prescribed altitude."

No matter what happens with the capsule during the booster phase of flight, during insertion into orbit, or during orbit, the flight recorders display exactly what is happening and—given a prescribed situation—what *will* happen. It's almost as if the men were able to "see" the capsule and understand everything that is happening with it at all times. In terms of what *will* take place, the situation is somewhat akin to your driving a car on a fast, curving slippery road. What will happen, for example, if you jam on your brakes at exactly 63.7 miles per hour while entering a turn with a side-acceleration factor of so many percentages over the force of one gravity? How far will you skid, when will the skid begin, where will the car stop, what will happen during every instant of the future time period? In terms of the capsule in which Glenn orbits, this is the kind of information that is always being obtained—except that for this space mission far more data are constantly displayed in terms of motions, accelerations, temperatures, velocities, and a hundred other items vital to the flight.

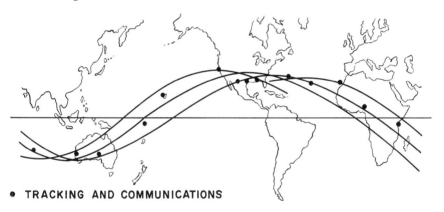

● TRACKING AND COMMUNICATIONS

Three orbits of John Glenn

All members of the flight team, instrumentation personnel, and selected members of the vehicle launching team, and the team handling voice communications with the astronaut in the capsule (as he passes within range of the Cape) are in a direct communications hookup with one another. In this fashion immediate contact is always assured, and there is no time lapse in getting information, requesting information, or initiating decisions among any part of the complex, interwoven command phase of Glenn's flight.

The "visual heart" of the tracking operation is a world map eight feet high by 26 feet wide (*see* illustration p. 76), which displays the orbital path of the capsule and the locations of all the world tracking stations. Colored rings which can flash with lights approximate the communication and tracking range of each station—showing exactly where the capsule is at any one time in relationship to its being tracked from the ground. Colors of individual rings indicate the operational status of each station; red means *critical malfunction,* yellow is *non-critical malfunction,* and green shows that operations are *normal.*

Within the boundaries of the map—visually available to everyone in Mercury Control—are facility status boxes. These displays indicate the status of various equipment at each of the international tracking stations, and the symbols include "readouts" such as: Command Control; Telemetry; Capsule Voice; Radar; Acquisition Aid; No Report Available; Voice Link; Computer; and Teletype.

Along the top of the global map, reading from left to right, are the indicators for: Greenwich Mean Time (Zulu); orbit number; countdown (hold and proceed); ground elapsed time; and time to retrofire. To the right and left of the giant map are trend charts—visual records of critical parameters of the capsule's flight.

Data recorded constantly throughout the flight include: astronaut's heart rate; astronaut's respiration rate; astronaut's body temperature; manual-control fuel remaining; automatic-control fuel remaining; DC volts; watt-hours remaining; oxygen quantity remaining (normal); oxygen partial pressure; carbon dioxide partial pressure; coolant quantity remaining; cabin air temperature; cabin pressure; suit inlet air temperature; suit pressure; and oxygen quantity remaining (emergency).

The world-wide tracking network includes two ships at sea: one along the equator in the Atlantic, off the African coast; the other in the Indian Ocean. More than 500 technicians man the

Antennas such as these at the Kauai, Hawaii, station are used to track the Mercury spacecraft in orbit. Kauai is one of 18 stations around the world—140,000 circuit miles built for NASA by the Western Electric Company.

global net, and they are all co-ordinated with the Goddard Space Flight Center in Maryland for real-time operation, as well as with Mercury Control at Canaveral. Each station is so located that it overlaps its tracking of the capsule to assure that Glenn will never be out of touch with the earth's surface at any one time.

The data of tracking are computed at the rate of "one thousand data bits" per *second,* and all information is obtained through the multiple systems of land lines, undersea cables, and radio circuits. There are a total of 140,000 actual circuit miles; these include 100,000 miles of teletype, 35,000 miles of telephone lines, and 5,000 miles of direct data circuits.

The world sites are:

Cape Canaveral	Bermuda
Grand Bahama Island	Grand Canary Island
Grand Turk Island	Atlantic Ship

Kano, Nigeria
Zanzibar Island (12 miles off
    Africa in Indian Ocean)   Kauai Island, Hawaii
Indian Ocean Ship   Guaymas, Mexico
Muchea, Australia   Point Arguello, California
Woomera, Australia   White Sands, New Mexico
Canton Island (between Hawaii   Corpus Christi, Texas
    and Australia)   Eglin, Florida

The Brain Center

Four IBM 7090 electronic computers—described by their oper-
ators as the "fastest digital computers in the world"—constitute
the brain core of Glenn's flight. One 7090 operates at Cape
Canaveral, the second at the Bermuda tracking station (which
has "emergency secondary command operation capabilities"),
and two computers at the Goddard Space Flight Center in Maryland.

The Goddard Center is a strange miracle of a space-age operation. Built into their computers are special information channels that permit the flight of Glenn to be carried out on the "real-
time basis." During the most critical parts of the mission in orbit,
the real-time channel is brought into maximum operation. It
allows command personnel to see their information displays on
the basis of not what happened several minutes ago, but *now*—
and in the immediate future.

"Critical," as applied to time elements of the orbital flight, includes the launch and the moment of insertion of the capsule
into orbit. During the later moments of flight, the critical time is
assumed to exist for re-entry, starting at the time that the decision is made from Cape Canaveral to return the capsule to
earth.

From the moment that the Atlas leaves the launch stand on
the Cape to begin the ascent, the Goddard 7090 computers instantly move onto a preprogramed operational basis. The mechanics of the flight have been programed into the computer
operation to take into consideration not merely the events that
are scheduled, but also any possible combination of events.

The moment the Atlas has its first motion, the computers operate on their real-time basis. They receive information from the capsule—the programing devices of the Atlas, such as its accelerometers, attitude indicators, and other performance-reading instruments that supply a complete running flight picture measured down to a tolerance of one half-second.

This information flows into Cape Canaveral and is almost instantaneously relayed to Goddard in Maryland. The flight-performance readings continue to Goddard until the moment that the sustainer engine of the Atlas booster shuts down, ending powered flight.

The next sequence of events *in space* includes separating the clamps that hold the capsule to the Atlas, and then firing the posigrade rockets to push the capsule away from the now-inert booster. Capsule turnaround is initiated for the capsule to move immediately into the retrofire position. All this is automatic.

There is a period of some 30 seconds after capsule separation from the booster that is considered an extremely critical time. During this period of one-half minute the Goddard computers must digest the final bits of data on the booster phase of the flight, and they must make—still within the same 30 seconds—a positive *Go—No Go* recommendation. The computers must display at Goddard—and simultaneously in Mercury Control at Cape Canaveral—the data that reveal whether or not the capsule is in orbit, or if it will re-enter the atmosphere before a complete orbit is achieved. If the reading is that the capsule has not been inserted properly into orbit, then Cape Control must decide—instantly—to fire the retrorockets, so that the capsule will re-enter in a preselected "abort recovery zone." Otherwise, Glenn might come plunging down from space to land in the midst of jungle, within mountains, or in an ocean area far from any immediate recovery.

Throughout the orbital period the 7090 computers operate constantly, but not on the critical basis of the "real time" requirements; these are commanded only during the launch, orbital insertion, and re-entry from orbit.

When the capsule approaches the end of the third orbit—coming up on Point Arguello—and is ready to begin its re-entry operations, the computers again snap into the real-time immediacy basis. If Cape Control needs to know what will happen if the retros are fired at any given instant, the computers will display immediately the exact position where the capsule will land. If Cape Control asks "if we fire the retros over this point—or that, or that—where will he land?" the computers electronically snap out the answer.

The Cape may request information on this type of basis: "As of this second, how do we refine this orbit to tell us exactly where the capsule will land in terms of longitude and latitude, so that we can notify the recovery forces to direct properly their ships and planes?"

"Everything is taken into consideration," explained a computer technician. "We consider the point of entry, atmospheric conditions, sea conditions—literally everything.

"One great big ball of wax, so to speak, is pushed into the computer banks, and these crank out every possible situation to be studied, and to form the basis on which rapid decisions can be made.

"The computer can be thought of as a digester of problems and a destroyer of question marks. During the flight, while the computers are 'idling,' they are always checking back, telling us every few minutes what a predicted impact point will be if the retros should fire at any moment.

"For example, if we fire the retros in the next recovery zone—where does Glenn land? We've got to have this kind of information always ready at our fingertips.

"Glenn may go into a normal flight path based on three orbits, considering all factors at a given instant. Then, let's say that something affects that orbit. What happens? Fractions of seconds are vital in this business. If something changes, we've got to have the computers cranking out constantly changing predictions—an absolute refinement of the situation—as of *now*. And '*now*' means the exact instant that you wish to know something."

The Final Hours

On February 18—two days before the launch—the booster technicians reported to Complex Fourteen to begin final loading of the kerosene fuel. Following the repairs to the Atlas interior, fuel had been loaded and dumped five times to check out the system. Now, however, they were "loading for bear." This was the fuel that—if the countdown went "all the way"—would be burned during a flight into space.

It was a quiet Sunday, and while the crewmen worked on Canaveral, Glenn drove from the Cape to attend morning worship services at Riverside Presbyterian Church in nearby Cocoa Beach, south of the launching site. This was the eleventh scheduled attempt, and even the most enthusiastic participants in the mission were hedging on their own convictions that "this time we're really going to get her off that pad."

At two o'clock Monday morning, the quiet routine of preparations increased in pace. The prelaunch activities for Atlas 109-D include what is called a split countdown. During the first half of the countdown, technicians swarmed over the booster, the capsule, and the escape system. Across Cape Canaveral, in Central Control, Mercury Control, at the abort recovery areas, in all tracking stations and film units, technicians began the familiar routine of once again setting up their equipment for the launch.

The Army was stirring. Pilots and mechanics checked out their airplanes and helicopters. An elite group shrouded from prying eyes prepared three graceful U-2 aircraft for flight. Stationed at Patrick Air Force Base 18 miles south of Cape Canaveral, the U-2's were part of an Air Force program making infrared studies in ballistic missile launchings from the Cape. They would also monitor Glenn's launch and flight.

Four hours later the first half of the split countdown ended. But the work continued. Several hundred newsmen were preparing—like everyone else, once again—their facilities to cover the launch. Television crews at the Cape checked over equipment, tested their communications lines to different points of Canaveral, and double-checked again their lines to all parts of the United States. One hundred and thirty-five million Americans would watch Glenn rush away from the earth at the actual time of launch.

Around the world, technicians made inspections of tracking and communications equipment.

Fifteen thousand men in the recovery areas pursued their normal vigil and . . . waited.

Thousands of people in cars and trailers continued to drift into the Canaveral area, setting up impromptu housekeeping on beaches, along side roads, on the edges of swamps. Some of them had been coming back for weeks, waiting for those fateful brief minutes of the launch.

At ten o'clock Monday morning Glenn appeared briefly in Cocoa Beach for a haircut. The tonsorial attention was more necessary than most people understood; Glenn's form-fitting helmet had been shaped to his head with a short crewcut—and this was hardly the time to discover any discomfort in wearing that helmet for several hours.

Monday night, February 19, Glenn went to bed at seven p.m. During the day he continued his training on the simulator for the Mercury capsule on Cape Canaveral, and studied his star charts and other aids.

The army of press began their moves into the Cape. Hundreds of newsmen would be awake through the night, preparing for the most intensive news coverage of *any* activity in history.

At 11:30 that night—only a half hour before midnight to begin the scheduled launch day—the blockhouse speaker of Complex Fourteen grated out the news: "The tower area is red. . . . The tower area is red." Explosive charges are placed in the Atlas. Except for the ordnance crewmen, the tower area is cleared. The men also install igniters in the propulsion system of the Atlas, and install the igniter for the capsule escape rocket.

At exactly 11:30 p.m. the second half of the split countdown begins. Launch is scheduled for 7:30 the following morning;

Mercury-Atlas 6 is now eight hours away from its planned "earliest possible time" of launch.

At midnight, during the past several weeks, weather briefings have been held at this time concerning the possibility of the launch the following morning. Walt Williams, directing the project, omits the briefing because of favorable reports from weathermen.

There is more optimism on this point than anyone officially wants to admit out loud. The recovery areas are all within minimum conditions, and they will almost surely remain this way.

This night I checked weather not at Canaveral, but up along a broad zone lying generally north and northwest. Heavy cloud layers were moving through these areas; Georgia was experiencing heavy rains and brief, high winds. Jacksonville and Tallahassee would be getting the same.

How quickly would the clouds pass over the Canaveral area to "open the sky" for optical access to the Atlas during launch?

Before John Glenn went to bed at seven o'clock Monday evening, the weathermen told him the chances were fifty-fifty—and no better. Almost certainly, however, February 21 would be *Go* all the way in terms of weather conditions.

But for Mercury-Atlas 6, a fifty-fifty chance is eagerly snatched at. If there are many more postponements, the orbital flight of the first American looks as if it will slip again, this time into the following month.

Dr. William K. Douglas—he and Dr. Stanley C. White, both Air Force lieutenant colonels, are the personal physicians to the astronauts—has scheduled Glenn's awakening for two o'clock the morning of February 20.

At that moment he will begin the first phase of his mission into orbit.

IV : *Mission into Orbit*

It is midnight at Cape Canaveral, Florida. The air is pleasant in temperature, but almost everything on the Cape is wet from the morning mists and salt spray of the ocean. The two hands of the clock are pointing at the figure 12 when in a monastic room in Hangar S on the Cape, Malcolm Scott Carpenter awakens quietly, dresses, and leaves for a brief drive to Complex Fourteen along the beachfront.

Carpenter—who will become the second American to orbit the earth—stands in the wings today while the prime astronaut of Project Mercury, John Herschel Glenn, Jr., occupies the stage center. Carpenter is the backup, or standby astronaut, and in this role he attends to the countless details that must be pursued to assure that everything will be in readiness—exactly to Glenn's needs and his liking—for the mission into orbit.

Glenn is still asleep when Carpenter calls Hangar S from the 12-story gantry tower at Complex Fourteen. He has checked out the capsule and reports that everything is fine. The booster also is in a *Go* condition.

The schedule calls for Glenn's awakening at about two o'clock. In the quiet darkness of his room the astronaut is awake by perhaps a half hour before his scheduled time. He has slept well, and he rests in the darkness, thinking about the mission to come, its steps and processes and procedures. At two o'clock, or several minutes afterward, Colonel Douglas comes into the room. The two men discuss Carpenter's call, and Douglas reaffirms that the count is moving along well.

Key astronauts in Mercury-Atlas 6. (Top photo) John Glenn (left) and Scott Carpenter, first and second Americans to orbit the earth. Carpenter was Glenn's backup pilot for the first manned orbital flight. They are seen here during preparations for MA-6. (Below) Glenn discusses countdown problems with Deke Slayton during mission postponement. Slayton was scheduled as prime pilot for MA-7; in doctor ordered switch he was moved out of immediate flight, with Carpenter stepping in for the mission.

At this moment the test-stand area itself at Complex Fourteen is under Condition Red. Technicians are closing the electrical connections to the capsule escape rocket. The countdown schedule moves along smoothly.

Everything is smooth except the weather. Over Canaveral the clouds are high and flat. The moon at times breaks through clearly; then it dissolves in mist and vanishes altogether, to reappear briefly at odd times. But this is not the weather that counts. These clouds are scheduled to blow out to sea. It is the weather to the north and northwest; during the long morning I receive weather reports from my contacts in different cities.

The weather now is everything. I make several bulletin reports during the night. Three weather officials of the Federal Aviation Agency, three contacts (all pilots who fly in this area), and myself come to a general agreement. The conditions will appear to be worse during early daylight, but a high wind should send the storm clouds, now to the northwest and north, well out to sea by mid-morning. Our joint estimates are that we will have no more than a sky obscuration of 20 to 40 per cent by 9:30, and if we have any luck with higher winds than expected, the sky should be excellent for a launch between 9:30 and ten o'clock.

At 20 minutes past two a.m. Glenn shaves and showers. Twenty-five minutes later he is joined by Donald K. ("Deke") Slayton, the astronaut scheduled to make the orbital flight after Glenn's mission. For Mercury-Atlas 6 Slayton performs extensive pre-flight work and capsule checkout duties. Now the two men meet for breakfast. Their meal includes orange juice, scrambled eggs, steak fillet, toast, jelly, and Postum.

At three o'clock Bill Douglas begins the medical examination. Glenn is in high spirits; his condition could not be better. The blood-pressure test reads 120/80. For all that is happening and that is about to happen, John Glenn might be sitting comfortably at home in Virginia and reading a book.

At 3:43 a.m. psychologists join Dr. Douglas in the physical examinations, and they give Glenn special tests to determine muscle co-ordination. Now they begin the "taping of the astronaut"—they tape to Glenn's body the electrodes that will measure

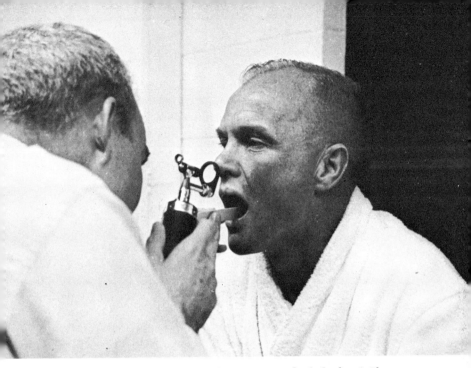

Dr. William Douglas goes through last-minute medical checks of Glenn early on the morning of the astronaut's space mission.

his temperature and heart rate and provide an electrocardiograph. This information will be recorded on the ground, before launch, and throughout the entire mission.

At five minutes to four, everything may come to a sudden stop. Walt Williams at this moment must make his decision for *Go* or *No Go*. Assistants bring to him all data on the flight, the weather at the moment and that predicted, the status of all tracking stations in the world-wide network, the condition of the astronaut, and other factors. The 7090 computers have digested every available factor and their readings also are made known to Williams. On the basis of all tests, reports, predictions, and his own analysis of all the factors involved, Williams gives a green light to the countdown. The schedule continues.

At four o'clock the loudspeakers on the Cape and throughout all areas involved announce a "hold" in the countdown for 90 minutes. At this moment the count is at T minus 120 minutes.

The hold is not a result of any difficulties, but has been built into the count as a precaution. During this period technicians are able to clean up any minor difficulties, to "nitpick" any problems. In this manner they attend to their needs without interfering with the progress of the countdown.

Since T minus 300 minutes the entire launch complex area has been under Condition Amber. The capsule is going through a final, extensive preflight checkout.

In the squat, domed blockhouse of steel-reinforced concrete, a staff of more than 100 skilled technicians works in concert under the direction of the Mercury-Atlas 6 Test Conductor—Thomas J. O'Malley. Behind this flight for O'Malley are 19 Atlas launchings. These give special meaning to his selection as the man from General Dynamics/Astronautics to conduct all NASA Atlas shots.

Overseeing everything that is going on—as he has from the very start of the operation—is B. G. McNabb, Operations Manager at Cape Canaveral for the entire Atlas program. "Mac" has waited a long time for this moment, and nothing escapes his practiced eye. He has been in the missile business for two decades, when the robot weapons in the United States were still embryonic creatures with dim futures.

At T minus 225 minutes the countdown checklist called for the entire Azusa system (the electronic tracking stations system that provides to the 7090 computers running reports of the Atlas position at any and all moments in flight) to check out. All stations report in, antennas are "homed to the bird," and they are "ready to track."

During the 90-minute built-in hold—with the count stopped at T minus 120—engineers make their final detailed checkouts of the propulsion system of three main engines and two sustainers. The two outboard boosters will fire with a combined rating of 300,000 pounds thrust, the center sustainer with 60,000 pounds thrust, and each of the two verniers with 1,000 pounds thrust. Scientists study and check out the autopilot, the guidance system, the intricacies of the telemetry system of the Atlas and the capsule, the fuel and oxidizer system, and auxiliary power units and systems.

Over the Cape there appear some bright, gleaming stars through breaks in the clouds. The newsmen keep looking up at the sky, seeking assurance that the clouds will clear and more stars will show. At 4:45 a.m. not a star is visible. The cloud deck is solid.

But a new source of light appears on the Cape. Twenty minutes past four o'clock the launch-stand workmen switch on the powerful floodlights. The scene is tremendous, a page out of science fiction. The red-and-white gantry looms 12 stories high, its colors clear and sharp. The blue-white lights pour brilliance over the tower and the booster it embraces, they shower light all across the area, and their beams glisten high above the Cape. Now the clouds are clearly visible as the beams of light vanish into their depths. Far to the right of Complex Fourteen a lone searchlight points straight up, a visual measurement of cloud heights. They are *low*.

Men look across Cape Canaveral, and many of them shake their heads slowly in mute wonder at the awesome scene. There, across Canaveral . . . is a spaceship, and a mighty rocket to hurl a man through vacuum with a speed of five miles per second.

Not so many years before tonight, the greater majority of the men and women here on the Cape to report the events as they happen had scoffed and ridiculed the idea of manned space flight. To them it was the impossible coming true before their eyes—as it was to most people everywhere.

At 4:30 o'clock Joe Schmitt, suit technician for the astronauts, prepares to assist Colonel Glenn in donning his silvery pressure suit, a space garment that costs more than $4,000. The suit weighs 20 pounds and is the result of intensive research and development by scientists of the B. F. Goodrich Company. Its surface is a dazzling aluminum-coated nylon-and-rubber material. It is a marvel in itself, incorporating oxygen-cooling and respiratory systems, automatic warning gauges and pick-ups for medical telemetering systems, to record physiological data of its wearer, and other scientific apparatus.

Four parts make up Glenn's space wardrobe—torso, helmet, gloves, and boots. Behind each unit lie hundreds of engineering changes and many thousands of hours of tests, under the direction of engineer Russ Colley. Few people realize that Colley has been in the spacesuit business since the early 1930's, when he produced a pressure suit for Wiley Post, who was anxious to fly his famous *Winnie Mae* into the stratosphere for a world altitude record. Post's suit was a cumbersome, rigid affair of heavy rubberized cloth stitched together on a home sewing machine.

Behind the serious moments of this morning of February 20 lies an incident that the spacesuit engineers look back upon with hilarity. In 1934 Wiley Post made an emergency landing because of engine trouble in the Mojave Desert. Post climbed from his airplane and waddled in his heavy, squat-helmeted pressure suit to a nearby road. A car was parked at the roadside. Post lumbered up and grunted a greeting to the driver. The motorist screeched in terror; he hid behind his car and then lit out into the desert in a cloud of dust. But fright weakened his knees and soon he was stumbling along. Post had to clutch the man by his shirt to make him stand still long enough to be convinced he wasn't being accosted by an alien from Mars.

Through the years, Colley kept improving his pressure suits. The peak of his work lies in different parts this morning in Hangar S. The torso is a closely fitted coverall shielding the entire body with the exception of the head and hands. The helmet attaches by a neck ring, and contains an anti-buffeting protection and the communications system. When sealed to the suit sleeves, the gloves form a continuous assembly, and custom-made pressure boots complete the space garment. The "hands" of the suit are especially tailor-made. They are curved with elaborately ribbed material—excepting the left middle finger. This finger is pressurized to remain rigid, so that the astronaut is able at all times to push buttons with it.

Joe Schmitt assists Glenn. The astronaut enters the suit by means of a pressure-sealing zipper located diagonally across the chest. A series of pleats and bellows tailored into the suit permit him to move his shoulders, arms, and legs without difficulty within the unpressurized suit. The sock endings are made of nylon stretch fabric with a thin ply of neoprene gum added. These feet are attached permanently to the inner layer of the suit.

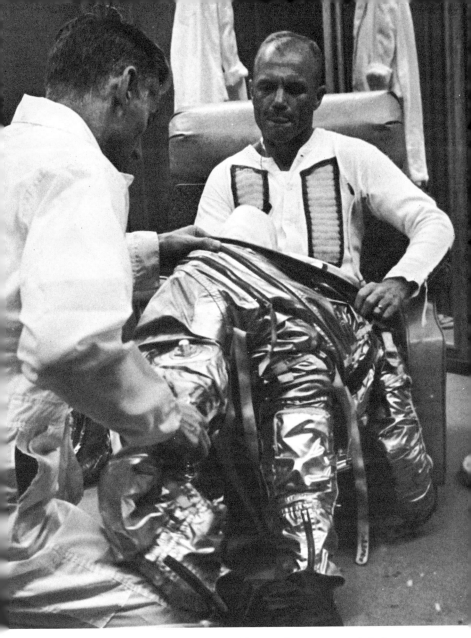

Suit technician Joe Schmitt assists Glenn in donning his pressure suit before leaving for Complex Fourteen. This was the morning of January 27; Glenn spent five hours in the capsule atop the Atlas before the mission was scrubbed.

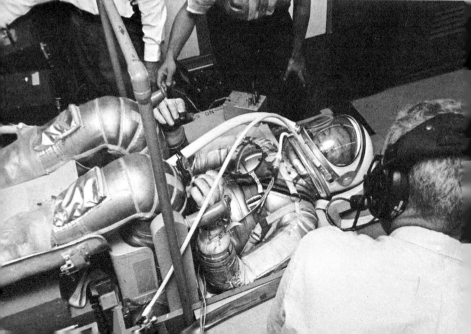

The suiting process takes 18 minutes. Glenn jokes with his fellow astronaut: "How about you getting into this suit, Deke?"

Joe Schmitt and Dr. Douglas conduct pressure tests of the suit. Glenn lies on his back in a contour-couch arrangement that duplicates his position in the capsule. The checkout is fine, and the suit is depressurized. As he walks from Hangar S later, and until he is ready to climb into the capsule, Glenn carries with him a portable air conditioner. Inside his suit he perspires quickly and profusely without the air conditioner; it is a vital part of his equipment.

The time is now one minute past five a.m. Accompanied by Bill Douglas and Deke Slayton, Glenn receives last-minute weather briefings. At 5:02 a.m. he appears in the doorway of Hangar S, then walks briskly to the large transfer van that will carry him to the launch pad. In his left hand is the air conditioner; with his right hand he waves to the crowd of people assembled in the hangar area. As he climbs the few steps into the van, he shakes hands with a technician.

Fifteen minutes later the transfer van looms from the darkness into the glittering, eerie world of the floodlit launch complex; the driver rolls cautiously to the side of the great gantry tower. He backs the van slowly into position for Glenn to move quickly from the van to the gantry elevator that will carry the astronaut 11 stories above the ground—capsule level, high over Cape Canaveral.

But Glenn waits inside the van. The hold is still at T minus 120 minutes, and it is being extended. Technicians have discovered that a rate beacon transponder in the Atlas guidance system is heating up too quickly and must be replaced. The rate beacon transponder in flight operates through the autopilot to provide reports of velocity data; the repairs will not be difficult.

Overhead, the weather remains threatening. Inside the van,

Launch-day preparations. (Above) Schmitt checks out Glenn's helmet connections. (Below) Lying on special contour couch in Hangar S, Glenn goes through complete suit pressurization checkout before leaving for the launch area.

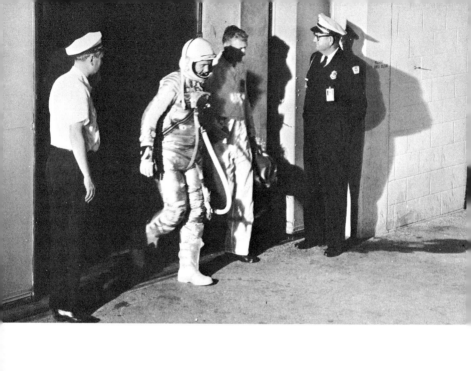

Glenn lifts the window blinds and stares out at the "great sight." The lights are brilliant; the rocket booster and gantry thrust upward in an other-world scene.

Glenn relaxes as he waits in a contour easy chair. The hold is extended 15 minutes.

One minute before six a.m., Glenn and a small group walk to the elevator at the foot of the gantry. The work crews pause to applaud enthusiastically and wave to the astronaut. Glenn waves back to the crews and nods; he shakes the hand of one ground crewman, and enters the elevator for the ride to level 11.

The capsule crew is ready, waiting to assist Glenn for "capsule insertion." But first Glenn hands some papers to a technician. Then he walks over to Carpenter, standing on the side, for a final handclasp with the man who has worked so hard to support Glenn's flight. No one knows better than Glenn the tremendous task fulfilled by Carpenter as backup pilot. For the flights of Shepard and Grissom, this was the same role that Glenn played in 1961.

At three minutes past six o'clock Glenn stands on a platform from which he will enter the capsule. A technician removes the plastic covers from his boots (to prevent his carrying dirt and dust into the capsule, which would float around in zero g). Glenn grasps the handle over the *Friendship 7* hatch and begins to ease his way into the capsule. His movements are careful and practiced as he wriggles into his cramped space vehicle and slides into the contour couch.

One minute later Glenn is in the capsule. Joe Schmitt leans in after the colonel to work on suit connections, to attach the biomedical sensors, and to begin a final suit-pressure check. Then the support breaks on a lip microphone within the helmet (used also as a respiration-rate indicator); it is necessary to replace this equipment, and proceedings are slightly held up.

Two walks with the same purpose in mind—one successful, the other a "scrub." In the top picture, Glenn leaves Hangar S the morning of January 27; hours later, he returned through this same door. In the bottom picture, Glenn has begun his triumphal trip. The date is February 20 . . . and Glenn is on his way to his successful launching.

Glenn wriggles his way through small hatch of Friendship 7 *on the day of launch. This unusual picture was taken with a 180° lens attached to a "fish eye" camera, mounted atop the 11th gantry deck.*

Glenn closes the helmet faceplate and runs through his suit-pressure check. He shakes hands for good luck with Joe Schmitt and several other men.

In front of Glenn there are 112 dials, switches, buttons, toggles, handles, meters—plus cameras, radio gear, oxygen supply, etc.—and a tiny felt mouse. The latter is the offering of Alan Shepard in a private joke with Glenn. Glenn runs through his checklist as the minutes go by quickly.

At 6:20 a.m. light begins to spread across the eastern horizon. It is a good sign, but directly overhead the clouds remains ominous and dark—and almost solid. But there comes the first breath of what we were forecasting—the wind from the north. The breeze picks up rapidly, and soon the clouds lower to the ground are beginning to increase their speed of movement over the surface.

Twenty-five minutes after six . . . The loudspeakers squawk: "We are resuming a live count. . . . We are now at T minus one-twenty . . . T minus one-twenty . . ."

Two hours to go in the countdown. The clouds are moving faster overhead. To the east of our position on the Cape the arc lights of Complex Fourteen stab brilliantly into the morning sky, shower back from the moving clouds. The moon is obscured from sight.

At 6:52 a.m. the count stands at T minus 93. To the north and east there are some patches of clearer sky, but overhead the clouds remain thick and cover the skies. One minute later there is sunrise—but the sun remains obscured by the clouds.

At 6:59 a.m. the technicians begin to install the hatch to the side of the capsule. Seventy-two explosive bolts must be inserted and secured firmly in place. By 7:02 a.m. another snarl occurs in the count—one of the explosive bolts breaks. A replacement takes time to find. A decision is made to remove the hatch and begin all over again with this procedure.

At 25 minutes past seven o'clock the count stands at T minus 60. One hour to go. A hold in the count is ordered to replace the broken hatch bolt and replace the hatch properly. This takes a total of 25 minutes.

While this goes on, Walt Williams receives a final weather check. The wind from the north blows more briskly now, and the promise of launch—despite the ominous skies overhead—looks better than before. Williams orders the count to continue; technicians begin their final checks of guidance, and start engine gimbaling tests.

By 7:52 a.m. the hatch is secure. The workmen start to leave the eleventh level. Overhead, the clouds are racing by the Cape, driven by winds from the north. The first big patches of blue sky are starting to show.

The count resumes—is picked up—at T minus 60. The time now is 8:05 a.m.

The crews start to pressurize the Atlas helium bottles. Workmen begin the process of clearing all gantry tower work levels, preparing to remove the gantry to its lock-and-hold positions.

Loud, booming horns begin to blow, warning everyone to clear the gantry. The deep sounds echo across all Cape Canaveral.

Fifteen minutes after the count is resumed—the time is now 8:20 a.m., and the count is at T minus 45—another 15-minute hold is ordered. The day before this morning a cold front passed through the Canaveral area. The change in pressure and temperature affected the tank capacity of the Atlas after it had been fueled. Ten gallons of kerosene are supplied to top off the fuel tank.

The gantry rolls back. Mercury-Atlas 6 stands by itself, tall and powerful, clear against a white-gray horizon to the east.

It is 8:35 a.m., T minus 45, and counting. The north wind picks up to 17 miles per hour.

Crews in the launch area begin to "chill down the plumbing." They are cooling the pipes for the transfer of liquid oxygen into the Atlas. The result is a shrill screaming from the effects of the supercold liquid oxygen (lox), which boils at 297° below zero Fahrenheit. The lox area is now under Status Red. The lox begins to feed to the oxidizer tank in the upper section of the Atlas. A hissing sound is added to the screaming pipes. The ground area becomes shrouded in billowing, swirling clouds of gox—gaseous oxygen—resulting from the oxidizer loading. By 8:40 a.m. plumes of white vapor are streaming from the vent valves in the side of the Atlas—bleeding pressure from the oxidizer tanks to prevent an undue buildup of pressure that might damage the thin-walled tanks.

In the capsule high above Canaveral, Glenn feels and hears the sounds of the events going on below him. The Atlas is a massive structure, yet because of its height and thin-walled structure heavy gusts of wind—states Colonel Glenn—actually cause the giant booster to sway slightly:

> *"The initial unusual experience of the mission is that of being on top of the Atlas launch vehicle after the gantry has been pulled back. Through the periscope, much of Cape Canaveral can be seen. If you move back and forth in the couch, you can feel the entire vehicle moving very slightly. When the engines are gimbaled, you can feel the vibration. When the tank is filled with*

liquid oxygen, the spacecraft vibrates and shudders as the metal skin flexes. Through the window and periscope the white plume of the lox venting is visible."

At the Forward Medical Area Marines start climbing into their helicopters—going on instant alert status in the event of an abort that would bring Glenn's capsule down into the waters off Cape Canaveral, or anywhere on the mainland itself. Army crews of amphibious vehicles are standing by. Air Force pararescue SCUBA teams are ready.

8:55 a.m.: The count is at T minus 25. The winds have turned the weather into a favorable situation in the launch area. The last clouds go scudding rapidly across the Cape skies, but the condition is *Go.* Downrange weather is *Go.* In Mercury Control the operations team completes a systems status check; everything is in the green and *Go.* At the blockhouse a steel door one foot thick rolls into place with a thud, and locks. The blockhouse seals completely. Downrange, optical and all systems are running through final checks and integration for the shot.

8:58 a.m.: Mercury Control (also titled Cape Control) receives word from the Cape Canaveral Central Control (Atlantic Missile Range controlling authority) that the Range Safety Officer has given his approval for the launch.

Almost at the same time the loudspeakers announce "T minus 22 *and holding . . .*" Technicians are having trouble with a valve in the liquid-oxygen fuel system in ground equipment.

9:23 a.m.: The count resumes; apparently the trouble with the valve is solved. "We are at T minus 22 and counting. . . ." It looks better and better. . . .

9:30 a.m.: From his capsule, high and alone, Glenn talks to Mercury Control. He has been listening to the conversation going on in Mercury Control. His voice comes over the intercom system. "I like the way you guys sound in there this morning," he says. The count continues, chopping away at the remaining minutes. The overhead is a clear, brilliant blue.

The count reaches "T minus 15 and counting . . ."

9:32 a.m.: The Marine rescue helicopters start their engines and prepare for takeoff.

9:33 a.m.: All data-recording inked styluses in Mercury Control and the blockhouse are standardized and time-co-ordinated for the rolling paper graphs. The countdown checklist continues. Tension builds up to a peak in the blockhouse where direct launch control is carried out.

9:35 a.m.: "T minus ten and counting . . ." The capsule, blockhouse, and Mercury Control report "all systems *Go.* . . ."

9:39 a.m.: Trouble! The count is T minus six minutes 30 seconds when an overload on the Bermuda station electronic digital computer blows a fuse. It is necessary to replace the fuse, and Bermuda estimates at least ten minutes for the repairs. Mercury Control requests that the time be cut; Bermuda replies in the affirmative that they will effect repairs within five minutes. It doesn't seem likely, but at 9:41 a.m. the impossible is accomplished in less time than anticipated, and the count resumes at T minus six minutes 30 seconds.

9:42 a.m.: "T minus five minutes and counting . . ." This is *it.* A series of events takes place now in staccato sequence. From this point for the next four minutes the blockhouse is at a peak in its operations.

All blockhouse air intakes are secured to prevent the possible intake of any toxic fumes.

A hold is announced; it is built into the count. In these brief moments each systems console reports to O'Malley a condition of *Go* or *No Go*. A decision is made to . . . *Go*.

The blockhouse commands chant out:

"*Inverter switch to ON* . . ." The internal AC power system of the Atlas is switched on to warm up the equipment.

"*Secure lox topping* . . ." Flow of liquid oxygen to the oxidizer tanks to keep the tanks full stops; the tank valves are sealed.

"*Start pressurization* . . ." The missile tanks are pressurized for flight status.

"*Water systems to ON* . . ." Water system for pouring water under high pressure into the curving flame bucket beneath the launch ring, where the Atlas flame is deflected away from the launch stand, is turned on.

"*Engine Arm Switch to ARM* . . ." All engine igniters are alive and armed.

"Atlas to internal power . . ." AC and DC internal power systems are ON.

In the capsule—90 seconds before the moment of liftoff—Astronaut Glenn moves quickly through some preplanned exercises to assure that his body is toned and ready for the mission. Then he places his left hand on the abort handle, a required part of his preflight checkout procedure.

The final sequence command crackles in the blockhouse:

"Systems Final Status Check . . ." One by one in the blockhouse Communications, Range Safety, Tracking, Aeromedical, Range, everywhere . . . the word comes back: *"Go!"*

The query snaps to Glenn in the capsule; his condition?

"Ready."

"T minus 60 seconds and counting . . ."

Thousands of people on the Cape take a grip upon themselves. Many involuntarily hold their breath. A hush descends over the Cape. . . .

"Atlas helium to internal . . ."

"Water to FULL FLOW . . ." Water smashes into the flame bucket at the rate of 35,000 gallons per minute.

"Autopilot to ARM position . . ." The flight programer is alive and ready to operate at launch.

The count is in *Prestart.* . . . The response everywhere is the same.

Go!

"Minus 50 seconds . . ." The range ready lights flick on to green. All tracking stations and the ships at sea are ready to acquire the spaceship with tracking equipment and to make communications contact.

"Thirty-five seconds . . ." In the blockhouse the command is: *"Eject spacecraft umbilical!"* The power cables kick away from the capsule. Glenn notes with satisfaction that the capsule periscope retracts to its position within the spacecraft. All systems are on internal battery power.

At T minus 18 seconds, O'Malley in the blockhouse stabs down on a black button on his control console. The automatic sequencer takes over the mission. The count continues under automatic control. If the electronic sensors detect anything wrong from this point on—even after the powerful booster engines ignite—they will automatically cut power and stop the procedure of launch.

"Vernier ignition!"

From the sides of Atlas 109-D, two lances of hard flame blaze suddenly.

"Ignition complete!"

The boosters and the sustainer engine erupt in a volcanic birth of golden flame.

"Mainstage!"

Thrust builds to full power. The Atlas disgorges a cataract of golden flame; it sweeps down, bends in the flame bucket, screams across the Cape as the water turns the fire into steam, and an enormous cloud hundreds of feet high rushes into the sky.

Fifty thousand people on the Florida beaches near the Cape freeze where they stand or sit. . . .

Three yellow steel clamps grip the Atlas, restrain its movement.

In the capsule, John Glenn feels the vibrations sweep through the Atlas. Then the roar comes to him, building steadily with each second.

Ice crystals and chunks break off the sides of the Atlas, falling free from the vibration of the motors.

Atlas 109-D is more powerful than anticipated; the propulsion system cries with 367,000 pounds thrust.

The umbilicals fly free from the booster.

The steel shackles snap back out of the way.

"First motion!"

"Liftoff!"

A blinding ball of golden fire, intense, shimmering along its edges, bulging downward into a teardrop at the bottom, pushes the Atlas upward from its pad. The fire washes down on the launch stand; Atlas moves only inches, then feet, then tens of feet. The flame spearing downward, trailing hazy flaming gases beneath the golden fire, now is clear of the launch stand.

Atlas is alive and free; her flame is free. . . . She begins to accelerate rapidly, pushing hard to escape from gravity.

The thunder rolls over Canaveral, a glorious and triumphant cry. Emotions break their bounds; people scream and shout; they leap up and down, wave clenched fists, cry out with the wonder of the sight before their eyes.

In the capsule, as Atlas tastes her freedom, Glenn reports: "Roger, liftoff . . . the clock is operating; we're on the way."

For the first two seconds of flight 109-D lifts straight up; then with the start of the third second the booster begins to roll to a northeast heading. Glenn feels the motion of the roll and he actually sees the change of direction by watching out his capsule window, through a mirror.

Glenn's voice as it comes into Mercury Control is tremulous. The flight is "bumpy" at this moment and his voice is vibrating.

The liftoff and launch are *flawless*. Atlas 109-D could not be performing better.

Twenty seconds after liftoff Glenn starts a backup clock on his wrist, then begins at once to check through cabin pressure, oxygen, fuel supply, battery ampere readings. Everything is going exactly as hoped for. Shepard reports from Mercury Control that the telemetry readings are in the green all the way; everything is perfect.

Watching Atlas rise into the heavens is a stunning, awesome sight, unlike any other, imbued with the significance of a man inside that capsule high atop the flaming rocket. I have seen so many of these giants fail—I watched the wreckage of Mercury-Atlas 3 spilling out of the blue skies back in April, 1961—that I am prepared, at any instant, to see this happen again, hoping against hope that it will not be so.

Atlas is perfect—flawless—all the adjectives one can think of. The golden color turns to orange, and then there is red along the edges by the booster flame. The great rocket is bending over steadily in flight, programing more and more away from the vertical.

In about one minute, or slightly less than this, the Atlas rushes into the lower edges of the stratosphere. The white contrail appears. For a moment the white trail is broken; then it becomes clean and wide, a white ribbon arrowing away from the earth.

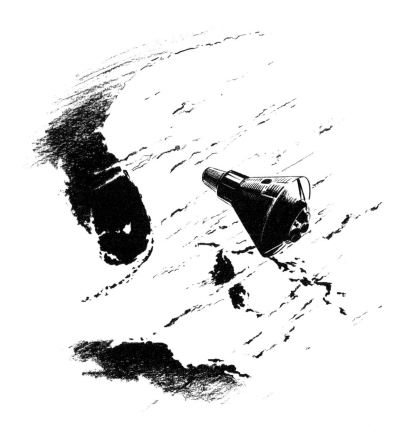

Mercury capsule in orbit over Florida

The mission into orbit is begun; Astronaut Glenn is on his way.

Exactly 129.6 seconds after liftoff the boosters jettison from the Atlas. At this moment a force six times that of gravity pushes Glenn down into his couch. He weighs nearly 1,000 pounds, but he experiences no difficulty from the enormous pressure squeezing his body.

At this point Glenn rushes into space at just over 7,000 miles per hour. The gravity forces drop back to 1.5 times that of normal; then they begin to build up again.

At 153.3 seconds the tower above the capsule jettisons. No matter what happens from this moment on, Glenn is committed to at least a ballistic flight path through space before returning to earth. His escape system now is only his capsule.

The escape rocket is gone. He has no personal parachute. The capsule is his means of sustenance in vacuum, in re-entry, in recovery. The man and the machine are as one.

At 301.4 seconds after he leaves the earth's surface, Glenn feels the sustainer engine and the verniers abruptly end their firing. The instant before this happens, he is under a pressure of 7.7g; his body weight is 1,232 pounds. Abruptly he is weightless.

Explosive bolts fire; clamps break free. Three small rockets blaze in vacuum. The capsule separates from the Atlas booster.

John Herschel Glenn, Jr., astronaut of Project Mercury, is the first American to enter orbit.

V: *Spaceflight and Snowflakes: The Official Report*

TWO MONTHS AFTER his three orbits of the earth in a flight that lasted four hours and 56 minutes from start to finish, and that included more danger and thrills than one is likely to find in science fiction, Astronaut John H. Glenn summarized the most vital findings of his mission.

"Weightless flight," he said, "was quickly adapted to, and was found to be pleasant and without discomfort. The chances of mission success are greatly enhanced by the presence of a human crew in the spacecraft. A human crew is vital to future space missions for the purpose of intelligent observation and actions when the spacecraft encounters expected or unexpected occurrences or phenomena."

Colonel Glenn put into words the intrinsic role of man better than had ever been done before. The fact that his remarks were tempered by the sight of flaming chunks tearing past his capsule window during re-entry—which could easily have been moments before a fiery death—lend special weight to his observations. They were made not under the best possible conditions, but under the threat of the worst.

Colonel Glenn reaffirmed after his orbital flight that "a manned vehicle provides a great advantage over an unmanned vehicle, *which is often deaf and blind to the new and the unexpected.*"

In discussing what occurred during that flight, we can only quote statistical data and the impressions of phenomena. But no man can give us certain details and features and impressions better than the man who was there—in this case, John Glenn. As he states, his special report on his orbital flight stresses "what I heard, saw, and felt during the orbital flight."

This, in his own words, is Astronaut Glenn's report of his three orbits around the planet earth on February 20, 1962:

Preparation, transfer to the launch pad, and insertion into the spacecraft went as planned. The technicians and I had been through the entry to the spacecraft many times.

As with every countdown, short delays were encountered when problems arose. The support for the microphone in the helmet, an item that had been moved and adjusted literally thousands of times, broke and had to be replaced. While the spacecraft hatch was being secured, a bolt was broken and had to be repaired. During this time I was busy going over my checklist and monitoring the spacecraft instruments.

Many people were concerned about my mental state during this and earlier delays, which are a part of preparation for a manned space flight. People have repeatedly asked whether I was afraid before the mission. Humans always have fear of an unknown situation—this is normal. The important thing is what we do about it. If fear is permitted to become a paralyzing thing that interferes with proper action, then it is harmful. The best antidote to fear is to know all we can about a situation. It is lack of knowledge that often misleads people when they try to imagine the feelings of an astronaut about to launch. During the years of preparation for Project Mercury, the unknown areas have been shrunk, we feel, to an acceptable level. For those who have not had the advantage of this training, the unknowns appear huge and insurmountable, and the level of confidence of the uninformed is lowered by an appropriate amount.

All the members of the Mercury team have been working towards this space flight opportunity for a long time. We have not dreaded it; we have looked forward to it. After three years we cannot be unduly concerned by a few delays. The important consideration is that everything be ready, that nothing be jeopardized by haste which can be preserved by prudent action.

The initial unusual experience of the mission is that of being on top of the Atlas launch vehicle after the gantry has been pulled back. Through the periscope, much of Cape Canaveral can be seen. If you move back and forth in the couch, you can feel the entire vehicle moving very slightly. When the engines are gimbaled, you can feel the vibration. When the tank is filled with liquid oxygen, the spacecraft vibrates and shudders as the metal skin flexes. Through the window and periscope the white plume of the lox (liquid oxygen) venting is visible.

Launch

When the countdown reached zero, I could feel the engines start. The spacecraft shook, not violently but very solidly. There was no doubt when liftoff occurred. When the Atlas was released there was an immediate gentle surge that let you know you were on your way. The roll to the correct azimuth was noticeable after liftoff. I had preset the little window mirror to watch the ground. I glanced up after liftoff and could see the horizon turning. Some vibration occurred immediately after liftoff. It smoothed out after about ten to 15 seconds of flight but never completely stopped. There was still a noticeable amount of vibration that continued up to the time the spacecraft passed through the maximum aerodynamic pressure or maximum q, at approximately $T + 1$ minute.

The approach of maximum q is signaled by more intense vibrations. Force on the outside of the spacecraft was calculated at 982 pounds per square foot at this time. During this period, I was conscious of a dull muffled roar from the engines. Beyond the high q area the vibration smoothed out noticeably. However, the spacecraft never became completely vibration free during powered flight.

The acceleration buildup was noticeable but not bothersome. Before the flight my backup pilot, Astronaut Scott Carpenter, had said he thought it would feel good to go in a straight-line acceleration rather than just in circles as we had in the centrifuge and he was right. Booster engine cutoff occurred at two minutes 9.6 seconds after liftoff. As the two outboard engines shut down and were detached, the acceleration dropped but not as sharply as I had anticipated. Instead, it decayed over approximately one-half second. There is a change in noise level and vibration when these engines are jettisoned. I saw a flash of smoke out the window and thought at first that the escape tower had jettisoned early and so reported. However, this flash was apparently deflected smoke coming up around the spacecraft from the booster engines which had just separated. The tower was jettisoned at two minutes 33.3 seconds, and I corrected my earlier report. I was ready to back up the automatic sequencing system if it did not perform correctly and counted down the seconds to the time for tower jettisoning. I was looking at the nozzles of the tower rockets when they fired. A large cloud of smoke came out but little flame. The tower accelerated rapidly from the spacecraft in a straight line. I watched it to a distance of approximately one-half mile. The spacecraft was programed to pitch down slowly just prior to jettisoning the tower and this maneuver provided my first real view of the horizon and clouds. I could just see clouds and the horizon behind the tower as it jettisoned.

After the tower fired, the spacecraft pitched slowly up again and I lost sight of the horizon. I remember making a comment at about this time that the sky was very black. The acceleration built up again, but as before, acceleration was not a major problem.

I could communicate well, up to the maximum of 7.7g at insertion when the sustainer-engine thrust terminates.

Just before the end of powered flight, there was one experience I was not expecting. At this time the fuel and lox tanks were getting empty and apparently the Atlas becomes considerably more flexible than when filled. I had the sensation of being out on the end of a springboard and could feel oscillating motions as if the nose of the launch vehicle were waving back and forth slightly.

Insertion into Orbit

The noise also increased as the vehicle approached SECO (sustainer engine cutoff). When the sustainer engine cut off at five minutes 1.4 seconds and the acceleration dropped to zero, I had a slight sensation of tumbling forward. The astronauts have often had a similar sensation during training on the centrifuge. The sensation was much less than during the flight, and since the spacecraft did pitch down at this point it may have been a result of actual movement rather than an illusion.

There was no doubt when the clamp ring between the Atlas and the Mercury spacecraft fired. There was a loud report and I immediately felt the force of the posigrade rockets which separate the spacecraft from the launch vehicle. Prior to the flight I had imagined that the acceleration from these three small rockets would be insignificant and that we might fail to sense them entirely, but there is no doubt when they fire.

Immediately after separation from the Atlas, the autopilot started to turn the spacecraft around. As the spacecraft came around to its normal aft viewing attitude, I could see the Atlas through the window. At the time I estimated that it was "a couple of hundred yards away." After the flight an analysis of the trajectory data showed that the distance between the launch vehicle and the spacecraft should, at this point, be 600 feet. Close enough for a rough estimate. I do not claim that I can normally judge distance so close. There was a large-sized luck factor in the estimate; nevertheless, the facts do give an indication that man can make an adequate judgment at least of short distances to a known object in space. This capability will be important in future missions in which man will want to achieve rendezvous, since the pilot will be counted on to perform the final closing maneuver.

Moment of triumph. (Above) *In Mercury Control, Alan Shepard flashes thumbs-up signal that the Atlas has lifted from the launch pad and the mission is on its way.* (Below) *In orbit at a speed of 17,545 miles per hour— 295 miles per second—Glenn studies his instrument panel.*

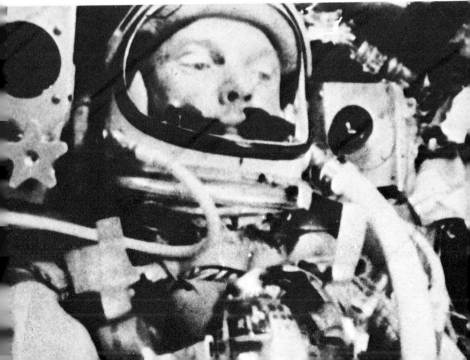

I was able to keep the Atlas in sight for six or seven minutes while it traveled across the Atlantic. The last time I reported seeing it the Atlas was approximately two miles behind and one mile below the spacecraft. It could be seen easily as a bright object against the black background of space and later against the background of earth.

Orbit

The autopilot turned the spacecraft around and put it into the proper attitude. After my initial contact with Bermuda I received the times for firing the retrorockets and started the check of the controls. This is a test of the control systems aboard the spacecraft. I had practiced it many times on the ground in the Mercury procedures trainer and the test went just as it had in the trainer. I was elated by the precision with which the test progressed. With your right hand you move the control stick, operating the hydrogen-peroxide thrusters to move the spacecraft in roll, pitch, and yaw. With your left hand you switch from one control system to another as the spacecraft is manually controlled to a number of precise rates and attitudes.

This experience was the first time I had been in complete manual control, and it was very reassuring to see not only the spacecraft react as expected, but also to see my own ability to control was as we had hoped.

Following this controls check I went back to autopilot control and the spacecraft operated properly on autopilot throughout the first orbit.

Thruster Problem

Because of a malfunction in a low-torque thruster at the end of the first orbit, it was necessary to control the spacecraft manually for the last two orbits. This requirement introduced no serious problems, and actually provided me with an opportunity to demonstrate what a man can do in controlling a spacecraft.

However, it limited the time that could be spent on many of the experiments I had hoped to carry out during the flight.

The Mercury flight plan during the first orbit was to maintain optimum spacecraft attitude for radar tracking and communication checks. This plan would provide good trajectory information as early as possible and would give me a chance to adapt to these new conditions if such was necessary. Other observations and tasks were to be accomplished mainly on the second and third orbits. Since the thruster problem made it necessary for me to control manually during most of the second and third orbits, several of the planned observations and experiments were not accomplished.

A number of questions have been raised over the ability of a man to use the earth's horizon as a reference for controlling the attitude of the space vehicle.

Throughout this flight no trouble in seeing the horizon was encountered. During the day the earth is bright and the background of space is dark. The horizon is vividly marked. At night, before the moon is up, the horizon can still be seen against the background of stars. After the moon rises (during this flight the moon was full), the earth is well enough lighted so that the horizon can be clearly seen.

Learning Period

With this horizon as a reference, the pitch and roll attitudes of the spacecraft can easily be controlled. The window can be positioned where you want it. Yaw, or heading reference, however, is not so good. I believe that there was a learning period during the flight regarding my ability to determine yaw. Use of the view through the window and periscope gradually improved.

To determine yaw in the spacecraft, advantage must be taken of the speed of the spacecraft over the earth which produces an apparent drift of the ground below the spacecraft. When the spacecraft is properly oriented, facing along the plane of the orbit, the ground appears to move parallel to the spacecraft longitudinal axis.

During the flight I developed a procedure which seemed to help me use this terrain drift as a yaw reference. I would pitch the small end of the spacecraft down to about –60 degrees from the normal attitude where a fairly good vertical view was available. In this attitude, clouds and land moving out from under me had more apparent motion than when the spacecraft was in its normal orbit attitude and I looked off toward the horizon.

At night with the full moon illuminating the clouds below, I could still determine yaw through the window but not as rapidly as in the daytime. At night I could use the drift of stars to determine heading but this took longer and was less accurate.

Throughout the flight I preferred the window to the periscope as an attitude reference system. It seemed to take longer to adjust yaw by using the periscope on the day side. At night, the cloud illumination by the moon is too dim to be seen well through the periscope.

Three times during the flight I turned the spacecraft approximately 180 degrees in yaw and faced forward in the direction of flight. I liked this attitude—seeing where I was going rather than where I had been—much better. As a result of these maneuvers my instrument reference system gave me an inaccurate attitude indication. It was easy to determine the proper attitude, however, from reference to the horizon through the window or to the periscope. Maintaining orientation was no problem, but I believe that the pilot automatically relies much more completely on vision in space than he does in an airplane, where gravity cues are available. The success with which I was able to control the spacecraft at all times was, to me, one of the most significant features of the flight.

Weightlessness

Weightlessness was a pleasant experience. I reported I felt fine as soon as the spacecraft separated from the launch vehicle, and throughout the flight this feeling continued to be the same.

Approximately every 30 minutes throughout the flight I went through a series of exercises to determine whether weightlessness was affecting me in any way. To see if head movement in a zero g environment produced any symptoms of nausea or vertigo, I tried first moving, then shaking my head from side to side, up and down, and tilting it from shoulder to shoulder. In other words, moving my head in roll, pitch, and yaw. I began slowly, but as the flight progressed, I moved my head more rapidly and vigorously until at the end of the flight I was moving as rapidly as my pressure suit would allow. . . .

In another test, using only eye motions, I tracked a rapidly moving spot of light generated by my fingertip lights. [At the end of each pressure-suit glove Colonel Glenn had a bright light for visual orientation and test purposes during the flight. M.C.] I had no problem watching the spot and once again no sensations of dizziness or nausea. A small eye chart was included on the instrument panel, with letters of varying size and with a "spoked wheel" pattern to check both general vision and any tendency toward astigmatism. No change from normal was apparent.

An "oculogyric test" was made in which turning rates of the spacecraft were correlated with sensations and eye movements. Results were normal. Preflight experience in this test and a calibration had been made at the Naval School of Aviation Medicine, Pensacola, Florida, with Dr. Ashton Graybiel, so that I was thoroughly familiar with my reactions to these same movements at 1g.

To provide medical data on the cardiovascular system, at intervals, I did an exercise which consisted of pulling on a bungee cord once a second for 30 seconds. This exercise provided a known workload to compare with previous similar tests made on the ground. The flight surgeons have reported the effect that this had on my pulse and blood pressure. The effect that it had on me during the flight was the same effect that it had on the ground—it made me tired.

Another experiment related to the possible medical effects of weightlessness was eating in orbit. On the relatively short flight of *Friendship 7*, eating was not a necessity, but rather an attempt to determine whether there would be any problem in

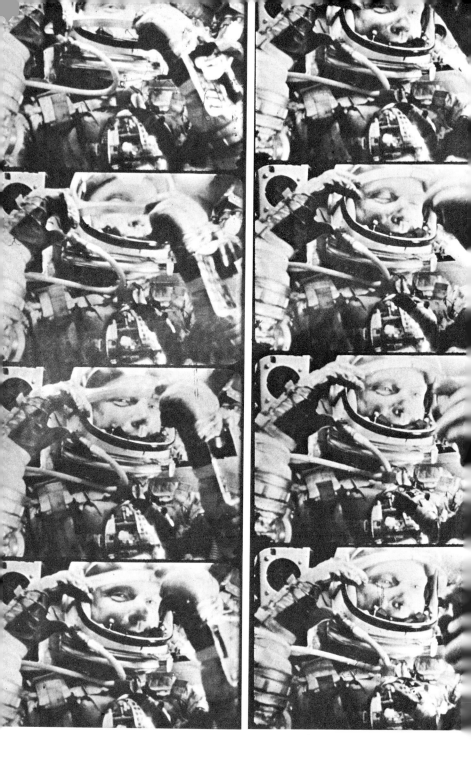

consuming and digesting food in a weightless state. At no time did I have any difficulty eating. I believe that any type of food can be eaten as long as it does not come apart easily or make crumbs. Prior to the flight, we joked about taking along some normal food such as a ham sandwich. I think this would be practical and should be tried.

Sitting in the spacecraft under zero g is more pleasant than under $1g$ on the ground, since you are not subject to any pressure points. I felt that I adapted very rapidly to weightlessness. I had no tendency to overreach nor did I experience any other sign of lack of co-ordination, even on the first movements after separation. I found myself unconsciously taking advantage of the weightless condition, as when I would leave a camera or some other object floating in space while I attended to other matters. This was not done as a preplanned maneuver but as a spur-of-the-moment thing when another system needed my attention. I thought later about how I had done this as naturally as if I were laying the camera on a table in a $1g$ field. It pointedly illustrates how rapidly adaptable the human is, even to something as foreign as weightlessness.

We discovered from this flight that some problems are still to be solved in properly determining how to stow and secure equipment that is used in a space vehicle. I had brought along a number of instruments, such as cameras, binoculars, and a photometer, with which to make observations from the spacecraft. All of these were stowed in a ditty bag by my right arm. Each piece of equipment had a three-foot piece of line attached to it. By the time I had started using items of the equipment, these lines became tangled. Although these lines got in the way, it was still important to have some way of securing the equipment, as I found out when I attempted to change film. The small canisters of film were not tied to the ditty bag by lines. I left

Glenn in orbit; an automatic sequence camera shows the astronaut as he opens his helmet faceplate and lifts the faceplate completely to the up position. The sequence begins at the top of the left column, reading down, then continues at the top of the right column, reading down.

one floating in midair while working with the camera, and when I reached for it, I accidentally hit it and it floated out of sight behind the instrument panel.

Color and Light

As I looked back at the earth from space, colors and light intensities were much the same as I had observed when flying at high altitude in an airplane. The colors observed when looking down at the ground appeared similar to those seen from 50,000 feet. When looking toward the horizon, however, the view is completely different, for then the blackness of space contrasts vividly with the brightness of the earth. The horizon itself is a brilliant, brilliant blue and white.

It was surprising how much of the earth's surface was covered by clouds. The clouds can be seen very clearly on the daylight side. The different types of clouds—vertical developments, stratus clouds, and cumulus clouds—are readily distinguished. There is little problem identifying them or in seeing the weather patterns. You can estimate the relative heights of the cloud layers from your knowledge of the types or from the shadows the high clouds cast on those lower down.

These observations are representative of information which the scientists of the U.S. Weather Bureau Meteorological Satellite Laboratory had asked Project Mercury to determine. They are interested in improving the optical equipment in their Tiros and Nimbus satellites and would like to know if they could determine the altitude of cloud layers with better optical resolution. From my flight I would say it is quite possible to determine cloud heights from this orbital altitude.

Only a few land areas were visible during the flight because of the cloud cover. Clouds were over much of the Atlantic, but the western (Sahara) part of Africa was clear. . . . In this desert region I could plainly see dust storms. By the time I got to the east coast of Africa where I might have been able to see towns, the land was covered by clouds. The Indian Ocean was the same.

Western Australia was clear, but the eastern half was overcast. Most of the area across Mexico and nearly to New Orleans was covered with high cirrus clouds. As I came across the United States I could see New Orleans, Charleston, and Savannah very clearly. I could also see rivers and lakes. I think the best view I had of any land area during the flight was the clear desert region around El Paso on the second pass across the United States. I could see the colors of the desert and the irrigated area north of El Paso. As I passed off the east coast of the United States I could see across Florida and far back along the Gulf Coast.

Over the Atlantic I saw what I assume was the Gulf Stream. The different colors of the water are clearly visible.

I also observed what was probably the wake of a ship. As I was passing over the recovery area at the end of the second orbit, I looked down at the water and saw a little "V." I checked the map. I was over recovery area G at the time, so I think it was probably the wake from a recovery ship. When I looked again the little "V" was under a cloud. The change in light reflections caused by the wake of a ship are sometimes visible for long distances from an airplane and will linger for miles behind a ship. This wake was probably what was visible.

I believe, however, that most people have an erroneous conception that from orbital altitude, little detail can be seen. In clear desert air, it is common to see a mountain range 100 or so miles away very clearly, and all that vision is through atmosphere. From orbital altitude, atmospheric light attenuation is only through approximately 100,000 feet of atmosphere so it is even more clear. An interesting experiment for future flights can be to determine visibility of objects of different sizes, colors, and shapes.

Obviously, on the night side of the earth, much less was visible. This may have been due not only to the reduced light, but also due partly to the fact that I was never fully dark adapted. In the bright light of the full moon, the clouds are visible. I could see vertical development at night. Most of the cloudy areas, however, appeared to be stratoform.

The lights of the city of Perth, in western Australia, were on and I could see them well. The view was similar to that seen when flying at high altitude at night over a small town. South of Perth there was a small group of lights, but they were much brighter in intensity. Inland there was a series of four or five towns lying in a line running from east to west. Knowing that Perth was on the coast, I was just barely able to see the coastline of Australia. Clouds covered the area of eastern Australia around Woomera, and I saw nothing but clouds from there across the Pacific until I was east of Hawaii. There appeared to be almost solid cloud cover all the way.

Just off the east coast of Africa were two large storm areas. Weather Bureau scientists had wondered whether lightning could be seen on the night side, and it certainly can. A large storm was visible just north of my track over the Indian Ocean and a smaller one to the south. Lightning could be seen flashing back and forth between the clouds but most prominent were lightning flashes within thunderheads illuminating them like light bulbs.

Some of the most spectacular sights during the flight were sunsets. The sunsets always occurred slightly to my left, and I turned the spacecraft to get a better view. The sunlight coming in the window was very brilliant, with an intense clear white light that reminded me of the arc lights while the spacecraft was on the launching pad.

I watched the first sunset through the photometer which had a polarizing filter on the front so that the intensity of the sun could be reduced to a comfortable level for viewing. Later I found that by squinting, I could look directly at the sun with no ill effects, just as I can from the surface of the earth. This accomplished little of value but does give an idea of intensity.

The sun is perfectly round as it approaches the horizon. It retains most of its symmetry until just the last sliver is visible. The horizon on each side of the sun is extremely bright, and when the sun has gone down to the level of this bright band of the horizon, it seems to spread out to each side of the point where it is setting. With the camera I caught the flattening of the sun just before it set. This is a phenomenon of some interest to the astronomers.

As the sun moves toward the horizon, a black shadow of darkness moves across the earth until the whole surface, except for the bright band at the horizon, is dark. This band is extremely bright just as the sun sets, but as time passes the bottom layer becomes a bright orange and fades into reds, then on into the darker colors, and finally off into the blues and blacks. One thing that surprised me was the distance the light extends on the horizon on each side of the point of the sunset. . . . I think that the eye can see a little more of the sunset color band than the camera captures. One point of interest was the length of time during which the orbital twilight persisted. Light was visible along the horizon for four to five minutes after the sunset, a long time when you consider that sunset occurred 18 times faster than normal.

The period immediately following sunset was of special interest to the astronomers. Because of atmospheric light scattering, it is not possible to study the region close to the sun except at the time of a solar eclipse. It had been hoped that from above the atmosphere the area close to the sun could be observed.

However, this would require a period of dark adaptation prior to sunset. An eyepatch had been developed for this purpose, which was to be held in place by special tape. This patch was expected to permit one eye to be night adapted prior to sunset. Unfortunately, the tape proved unsatisfactory and I could not use the eyepatch. Observations of the sun's corona and zodiacal light must await future flights when the pilot may have an opportunity to get more fully dark adapted prior to sunset.

. . . The biggest surprise of the flight occurred at dawn. Coming out of the night on the first orbit, at the first glint of sunlight on the spacecraft, I was looking inside the spacecraft checking instruments for perhaps 15 or 20 seconds. When I glanced back through the window my initial reaction was that the spacecraft had tumbled and that I could see nothing but stars through the window. I realized, however, that I was still in the normal attitude. The spacecraft was surrounded by luminous particles.

These particles were a light yellowish green color. It was as if the spacecraft were moving through a field of fireflies. They were about the brightness of a first magnitude star and appeared to vary in size from a pinhead up to possibly 3/8ths inch. They were about eight to ten feet apart and evenly distributed through the space around the spacecraft. Occasionally, one or two of them would move slowly up around the spacecraft and across the window, drifting very, very slowly, and would then gradually move off, back in the direction I was looking. I observed these luminous objects for approximately four minutes each time the sun came up.

During the third sunrise I turned the spacecraft around and faced forward to see if I could determine where the particles were coming from. Facing forwards I could see only about ten per cent as many particles as I had when my back was to the sun. Still, they seemed to be coming toward me from some distance so that they appeared not to be coming from the spacecraft. Just what these particles are is still subject to debate and awaits further clarification.

. . . After having turned around on the last orbit to see the particles, I maneuvered into the correct attitude for firing the retrorockets and stowed the equipment in the ditty bag.

This last dawn found my attitude indicators still slightly in error. However, before it was time to fire the retrorockets the horizon-scanner slaving mechanism had brought the gyros back to orbit attitude. I crosschecked repeatedly between the instruments, periscope presentation, and the attitude through the window.

Although there were variations in the instrument presentations during the flight, there was never any difficulty in determining my true attitude by reference to the window or periscope. I received a countdown from the ground and the retrorockets were fired on schedule just off the California coast.

I could hear each rocket fire and could feel the surge as the rockets slowed the spacecraft. Coming out of zero-g condition, the retrorocket firing produced the sensation that I was accelerating back toward Hawaii. This sensation, of course, was an illusion.

Following retrofire, the decision was made to have me re-enter with the retro package still on because of the uncertainty as to whether the landing bag had been extended. This decision required me to perform manually a number of the operations which are normally automatically programed during the re-entry. These maneuvers I accomplished. I brought the spacecraft to the proper attitude for re-entry under manual control. The periscope was retracted by pumping the manual retraction lever.

As deceleration began to increase I could hear a hissing noise that sounded like small particles brushing against the spacecraft.

Due to ionization around the spacecraft, communications were lost. This had occurred on earlier missions and was experienced now on the predicted schedule. As the heat pulse started there was a noise and a bump on the spacecraft. I saw one of the straps that holds the retrorocket package swing in front of the window.

The heat pulse increased until I could see a glowing orange color through the window. Flaming pieces were breaking off and flying past the spacecraft window. At the time, these observations were of some concern to me because I was not sure what they were. I had assumed that the retropack had been jettisoned when I saw the strap in front of the window. I thought these flaming pieces might be parts of the heat shield breaking off. We know now, of course, that the pieces were from the retropack.

There was no doubt when the heat pulse occurred during re-entry but it takes time for the heat to soak into the spacecraft and heat the air. I did not feel particularly hot until we were getting down to about 75,000 to 80,000 feet. From there on down I was uncomfortably warm, and by the time the main parachute was out I was perspiring profusely.

The re-entry deceleration of 7.7g was as expected and was similar to that experienced in centrifuge runs. There had been some question as to whether our ability to tolerate acceleration might be worse because of the four and a half hours of weightlessness, but I could note no difference between my feeling of deceleration on this flight and my training sessions in the centrifuge.

After peak deceleration, the amplitude of the spacecraft oscillations began to build. I kept them under control on the manual and fly-by-wire systems until I ran out of manual fuel. After that point, I was unknowingly left with only the fly-by-wire system and the oscillations increased; so I switched to auxiliary damping, which controlled the spacecraft until the automatic fuel was also expended. I was reaching for the switch to deploy the drogue parachute early in order to reduce these re-entry oscillations, when it was deployed automatically. The drogue parachute stabilized the spacecraft rapidly.

At 10,800 feet the main parachute was deployed. I could see it stream out behind me, fill partially, and then as the reefing line cutters were actuated it filled completely. The opening of the parachute caused a jolt, but perhaps less than I had expected.

The landing deceleration was sharper than I had expected. Prior to impact I had disconnected all the extra leads to my suit, and was ready for rapid egress, but there was no need for this. I had a message that the destroyer *Noa* would pick me up within 20 minutes. I lay quietly in the spacecraft trying to keep as cool as possible. The temperature inside the spacecraft did not seem to diminish. This combined with the high humidity of the air being drawn into the spacecraft kept me uncomfortably warm and perspiring heavily. Once the *Noa* was alongside the spacecraft, there was little delay in starting the hoisting operation. The spacecraft was pulled part way out of the water to let the water drain from the landing bag.

During the spacecraft pickup, I received one good bump. It was probably the most solid jolt of the whole trip as the spacecraft swung against the side of the ship. Shortly afterwards the spacecraft was on the deck.

I had initially planned egress out through the top, but by this time I had been perspiring heavily for nearly 45 minutes. I decided to come out the side hatch instead.

General Remarks

Many things were learned from the flight of *Friendship 7*. Concerning spacecraft systems alone, you have heard many reports . . . that have verified previous design concepts that need remedial action.

Dramatic photograph shows the exact moment when a Mercury capsule slams into the Atlantic Ocean. The capsule has "splashed" with a large shower of spray; at the same moment the 63-foot Radioplane parachute breaks free of the spacecraft.

Friendship 7 floats in the Atlantic with John Glenn aboard. The destroyer USS Noa retrieved the spacecraft 21 minutes after impact.

Now, what can be said of man in the system?

Of major significance is the probability that much more dependence can be placed on the man as a reliably operating portion of the man-spacecraft combination. In many areas his safe return can be made dependent on his own intelligent actions. Although a design philosophy could not be followed up to this time, Project Mercury never considered the astronaut as merely a passive passenger.

These areas must be assessed carefully, for man is not infallible, as we are all acutely aware. As an inflight example, some of you may have noticed a slight discrepancy between launch photographs of the pilot and similar re-entry views. The faceplate on the helmet was open during the re-entry phase. Had cabin pressure started to drop, I could have closed the faceplate in sufficient time to prevent decompression, but nevertheless a faceplate-open re-entry was not planned.

On the ground, some things would also be done differently. As an example, I feel it more advisable in the event of suspected malfunctions, such as the heat-shield-retropack difficulties, that require extensive discussion among ground personnel to keep the pilot updated on each bit of information rather than waiting for a final clearcut recommendation from the ground. This keeps the pilot fully informed if there would happen to be any communication difficulty and it became necessary for him to make all decisions from onboard information.

Many things would be done differently if this flight could be flown over again, but we learn from our mistakes. I never flew a test flight on an airplane that I didn't return wishing I had done some things differently.

Even where automatic systems are still necessary, mission *reliability* is tremendously increased by having the man as a backup. The flight of *Friendship 7* is a good example. This mission would almost certainly have not completed its three orbits, and might not have come back at all, if a man had not been aboard.

The flight of the *Friendship 7* Mercury spacecraft has proved that man can *adapt* very rapidly to this new environment. His senses and capabilities are little changed in space. At least for the 4.5-hour duration of this mission, weightlessness was no problem.

Man's adaptability is most evident in his powers of observation. He can accomplish many more and varied experiments per mission than can be obtained from an unmanned vehicle. When the unexpected arises, as happened with the luminous particles and layer [atmospheric layer] observations on this flight, he can make observations that will permit more rapid evaluation of these phenomena on future flights. Indeed, on an unmanned flight there likely would have been no such observations.

Most important, however, the future will not always find us a power limited as we are now. We will progress to the point where missions will not be totally preplanned. There will be choices of action in space, and man's intelligence and decision-making capability will be mandatory.

Our recent space efforts can be likened to the first flights at Kitty Hawk. They were first unmanned but were followed by manned flights, completely preplanned and of a few seconds duration. Their experiments were, again, power limited, but they soon progressed beyond that point.

Space exploration is now at the same stage of development.

[The foregoing, with some technical material deleted, constitutes the official report of Lt. Colonel John H. Glenn, Jr., on his three-orbit mission of Mercury-Atlas 6.]

VI: *Sidelines of Mercury-Atlas 6*

THE OFFICIAL REPORT of Astronaut John H. Glenn, Jr., for Mercury-Atlas 6 tells the intrinsic purpose and meaning of the three-orbit space flight. It is not the entire story, however, for in so vast and stirring an enterprise there are many details which, although as important as many others, seem to become obscured in the ponderous size of the effort and the numbers of people involved. Some of these details are precious moments of history, and the author feels that they have special significance to the telling of this story.

For example, there was what Mercury Control personnel came later to describe as "a moment of horror in the launching." During the ascent hearts stopped beating for an instant. Major General O. J. Ritland, USAF, explained that: "At about 150 seconds after launching the pen that tracks the plot [of the Atlas course in flight] faltered . . . *and we had no plot.*"

That is the kind of situation that causes the Range Safety Officer to stab his finger down on a button marked DESTRUCT. It means that the Atlas has suddenly veered off its assigned course of flight and is then creating a serious hazard to the lives of people. The immediate cure for this situation is to destroy the Atlas, to set off its explosive charges.

At the moment the pen faltered, the booster was 150 seconds from liftoff. And then, in that harrowing moment in Mercury Control, a technician showed almost immediately that it was the *pen* that faltered, and not the plot—and the sighs of relief were like a "cool breeze in that room!"

It is not generally known that Glenn was permitted to make his third orbit only by the strange coincidence that his many postponements in the flight finally turned into an advantage. The requirement of at least three hours of full daylight after the astronaut landed in the sea was for safety purposes in search and recovery. The time schedule for this flight was specific: after 9:30 a.m. the mission would be limited to only two orbits.

But Glenn launched at 9:47 a.m. . . . . The decision to move ahead with the three full orbits, in respect to the time requirements, stemmed directly from the long postponements. When MA-6 was originally scheduled, the 9:30 a.m. cutoff point for three orbits was rigid. But by February 20, the days were so much longer that an additional 30 minutes was available in latest possible launch times—and so the 9:30 a.m. cutoff time became, for February 20, 10:00 a.m. Had Glenn launched on his original date of January 16, MA-6 would have been a two-orbit space mission.

Inadequate attention has been paid to the wonderful people of Perth, Australia. As he passed over that city and saw its gleaming lights in the darkness far below him, Colonel Glenn called via radio to Astronaut L. Gordon Cooper:

"Just to my right I can see a big pattern of light. Apparently right on the coast . . ."

Cooper explained: "That is Perth and Rockingham you see there."

Glenn: "The lights show very well. On down to the south and inland, I can see lights. There are two, actually four patterns in that area. Also coming in sight in the window now another one, almost down under me. The lights are very clear from up here."

Then Glenn asked Cooper to "Thank everybody for turning them on."

When the Voice of America broadcast Colonel Glenn's thanks directed to Perth, the city rejoiced in the message. Before the flight, the citizens of Perth and the surrounding communities in the metropolitan and suburban areas promised to turn themselves into as great a source of light as they could until Astronaut Glenn was safely back on earth.

In Perth every street light, every neon sign, every bulb was

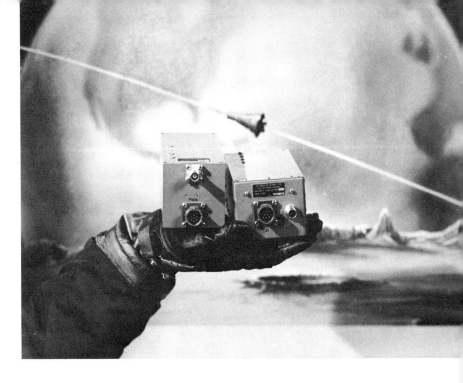

Link between two worlds . . . Light enough and small enough to be held in a man's hand (above), these two Collins radio transceivers were used by Glenn to maintain radio contact with earth tracking stations and (below) Mercury Control. At left is Dr. Bill Douglas, center is Deke Slayton, and at right is Alan Shepard, in voice communications with Glenn.

blazing with light. People rigged up special lights on their lawns and on their homes; they mounted white sheets and silver reflectors to increase the intensity of the illumination.

And they shouted in joy when they learned that for the first time in history a man in space had looked down upon the earth to see and to acknowledge a glittering message to him from an entire city.

When the Mercury astronauts work at Cape Canaveral, they live at the Holiday Inn Motel along Highway A1A in Cocoa Beach, south of the Cape. This has been their "unofficial headquarters" during their Cape visits. In recognition of Glenn's flight, the front-lawn marquee of the Holiday carried in theater-like presentation the message: "Hopes and prayers of free world are with Col. John Glenn." Between the marquee and the motel proper stretched a long line of colorful flags from 98 different nations—although it was extremely difficult to discover what major space interests or activities there were to be found in Mali, Portugal, Chile, Bulgaria—*et al.*

And as for the first country to launch an earth satellite, send a rocket to the moon, send a man into orbit—*two* men into orbit— why, the flag of the USSR was for some strange and never-explained reason absent from the lineup.

The culinary aspects of Glenn's orbital flight left much to be desired, but eating in space (Glenn had no opportunity to drink any liquids) was a vital part of the flight. Yuri Gagarin had partaken of food; Gherman Titov had eaten three complete space meals. Glenn had opportunity only once to eat, about 20 minutes after he left Cape Canaveral—going straight up.

Glenn ate his space snack at 10:09 a.m. as he sailed over the tracking station at Kano, Nigeria in Africa. He ate a two-course menu of a beef-vegetable mixture and applesauce. These were in special tubes that resembled giant toothpaste tubes. The food inside was in semi-solid form—something like baby food—only it contained the tastier elements of seasoning and sugar. Each tube has a cap with a metal seal inside the neck. Glenn removed the cap and screwed on a special nozzle that broke the seal. He lifted his helmet faceplate, placed the nozzle in his mouth, and squeezed the tube. As he related in his official report, eating in zero g gave him no problems.

Inside the capsule, Glenn carried a total of 3,000 calories of food. He had quick-energy sugar tablets, and six pounds of water in two flat bottles, each with its own tube for sucking out the water, like drinking through a straw.

Glenn also carried special drugs with him already placed in spring-loaded hypodermics. The drugs included morphine to act as a painkiller, wyamine for use as a stimulant, and an anti-motion-sickness drug known as tigan. Glenn did not use any of these. For medical research his suit was equipped with a plastic tube and container; Glenn was scheduled during the flight to urinate as one of his biomedical performance tasks.

In his official report Glenn appears to minimize the problems with the stabilization system of the spacecraft, but these problems were anything but minimal in orbit. Glenn's control problems began on his first orbit (and they were similar to the problems with the MA-5 flight with the chimpanzee Enos; a roll jet became plugged on that mission on November 29, 1961, and ground command terminated the flight after two orbits) as the capsule neared the tracking station at Guaymas, Mexico.

At the time the capsule attitude was being maintained by the automatic system. The automatic system has four jets for control in roll, four for pitch in up and down, and four for yaw in right and left. Of the four jets in each set, two operate with one pound thrust and the other two with 24 pounds thrust. During the orbital flight all normal maneuvers are carried out with the one-pound jets (or thrusters); these are adequate to the task, and they do not use nearly as much fuel as do the larger reaction jet pairs.

Glenn noticed suddenly that his spacecraft was drifting in yaw to the right at about one degree per second. When it reached a yaw of 20 degrees, without corrective response from the smaller jets, the 24-pound-thrust jets automatically kicked in to reorient the capsule to the proper attitude.

The automatic system might have been able to continue the necessary attitude control (although some engineers dispute this). But even were this the case, it seemed almost certain that by the time the three orbits were completed, the capsule's fuel supply of hydrogen peroxide would have been exhausted. And that meant no fuel for stabilization during the extremely critical re-entry period.

Glenn made the decision to take over capsule attitude control manually. He switched to his fly-by-wire control mode. This is a manual-control system which is connected through the auto-pilot from the three-axis control stick that Glenn used. When Glenn moved the stick, the movement was translated into an electrical signal; the signals in turn actuated valves in the control system to release spurts of hydrogen peroxide.

Later in the flight, Glenn transferred his control mode to the completely independent manual system. This uses six different jets—two for each axis of movement. It has the decided advantage of conserving fuel, because the extent of movement of the control stick determines how much hydrogen peroxide is released each time Glenn maneuvered his capsule in its attitude. Thus he minimized his danger of consuming an excessive quantity of hydrogen peroxide.

Glenn's conversations from the capsule in orbit on this matter with Alan B. Shepard, at Mercury Control on the Cape:

Glenn: "I am going on fly-by-wire so I can control more accurately. It just started as I got to Guaymas and it appears to drift off, yaw to the right at about one degree per second. It would go over to an attitude of about 20 degrees, then hold, and then when it hits at about a 20-degree point, it then goes back into orientation mode and comes back to zero, and it was cycling back and forth in that mode. I am on fly-by-wire now, I am controlling manually. . . . What appears to have happened is, I believe I have one-pound thrust in left yaw, so it drifts over out of limits and then hits it with the high thrust."

Shepard: "We concur here, recommend you remain fly-by-wire."

Glenn: "Roger, am remaining fly-by-wire. Controlling manually on fly-by-wire, having no trouble controlling, very smooth and easy, it controls very nicely. Fly-by-wire autogyro is normal."

Later, Glenn and Walter M. Schirra discussed the situation as Glenn passed over California:

Glenn: "I had some erratic ASCS [1] operation and I caged and uncaged on the night side and it appears to be working very well now, although I was drifting again in roll a moment ago. It appears to have corrected itself in roll, without my caging it again. . . ."

Schirra: ". . . we recommend that you allow capsule to drift on manual control to conserve fuel."

This was for the final orbit. To prevent the danger of exhausting his fuel prior to the critical re-entry period, Glenn did not attempt through this orbit to maintain exact capsule attitude. Instead, he placed the capsule on automatic control, and then allowed the capsule to "drift" in attitude without making constant corrections; he resumed control as the last phase of his orbital flight.

As to the extent of the time lost for scientific experiments in the final two-thirds of the flight, at his press conference at Cape Canaveral after the mission, Glenn explained that "we spent most of the last two orbits . . . largely concentrating, probably 90 per cent of the time, on the control system."

Comments excerpted from Colonel Glenn's press conference at Canaveral contain items of special interest, as follows:

Question: ". . . what did the stars and the earth look like up there?"

Glenn: "Well, stars—I was a little bit surprised. I think I . . . expected to see the stars in greater quantity and greater numbers than I had seen them before. The nearest thing I could compare it to, and did compare it to during debriefing, was the—I think— if you've been out in the desert on a very clear brilliant night when there's no moon up and the stars just seem to jump out at you, that's just about the way the stars look.

". . . They were not blinking. They came through very clear and straight shining light, and there was no flickering on and off. But other than that, it looked very similar to looking at the sky on a very, very clear night in the desert."

[1] Automatic stabilization and control system.

A question was asked on Glenn's ability to see details on the earth's surface. To this question, also discussed in his official report, he answered at length:

Glenn: "You can see different patterns in the ocean currents, like the Gulf Stream, for instance. You can see the changing colors there. You can see on the earth . . . one area that I could observe very clearly was the area northwest of El Paso.

". . . that's an area where there's a lot of desert with a big irrigated area that comes down a valley northwest of El Paso, and that stood out very much. You can see the squares of the irrigated areas from this distance.

"I wouldn't guarantee that I was seeing the smallest irrigated squares that they have—each individual patch—but the larger irrigated squares probably had major dikes around them. I could see these very clearly.

". . . The Salton Sea area was very visible. . . . you can see blocks or squares in towns. We had figured before we probably would be able to pick out items down to, say 100 to 150 yards long, and I think this was probably a fair estimate."

Question: "In the future we have planned to experiment with a so-called rendezvous or docking technique in space, and it's going to be important to know how your depth perception is in space. Did you have any trouble figuring out just where the booster was when it started leaving the capsule?"

Glenn: "No. This was quite a sight. Right at turnaround we separated from the booster . . . and as it [the spacecraft] swung around, the booster was sitting there, probably within 100 yards. Very visible, very clear.

"We talked about this during debriefing. If I had the capability of having a little thrust to move over that direction, could I have maneuvered toward it? I think very definitely you could. I don't think this would be any problem at all from that distance.

"Now the booster, because of its different velocity, assumes a little different orbit than I had, and it went slightly under me and was passing ahead of me and in a lower orbit the last time I saw it. This was out pretty well toward the coast of Africa, and I didn't see it again after that."

Question: "What was the noise level inside the capsule in orbit?"

Glenn: "The noise level in the capsule was very similar to what it is on the pad out here. You have the whine of the inverters, the gyros, the valves, the hiss of oxygen in the helmet. It's not a loud intensity. . . ."

Question: "Did you use the little red lights at the end of your fingertips on your gloves?"

Glenn: "Yes. I found these very handy. . . . I could turn them on and off with a little switch on the back of the hand. The little fingertip lights are very small bulbs, for looking at charts, for checking the maps, and in the tight capsule lighting we have, these turned out to be very handy and I used them repeatedly. I like them very much and am glad we decided to put them on."

There are, of course, many different "sidebars"—stories of human interest and of interesting technical detail—to the flight of John Glenn.

But certainly a few words must be said for the reaction of B. G. McNabb of General Dynamics/Astronautics, "father" of the Atlas program at Cape Canaveral, who brought the great rocket from its earliest growing pains to the realization of his long-cherished dream—watching his Atlas send an American into orbit, and being there, right at the Cape, when the news came in that the astronaut was down, safe and sound.

As Glenn orbited the earth from 100 to 162 miles high, "Mac" joined us at the press site on the Cape. Finally there came the moment when Glenn was passing overhead, already descending, rushing down through the atmosphere. All of us scanned the bright skies over the Cape, hoping to see a telltale line, a streak in the skies, that would be evidence of the re-entry flight. But nothing was visible.

Then, later, Gatha Cottee of NASA's Cape Canaveral team placed a small Mercury spacecraft model against a giant map, pinpointing the area where *Friendship 7* had dropped safely into the sea, where the destroyer *Noa* was rushing to retrieve Glenn from the water.

Confirmation of the "splashdown" boomed out over the press-site loudspeakers, from Mercury Control. The sound was still echoing throughout the area when "Mac" threw back his head and gave out a shout of pure jubilation. It was a bit incoherent, and all of us there agree that "Mac's" victory cry was definitely:

"*ARRAGHHH!*"

But then . . . he was *very* happy!

VII : *"Segment 51"*

AT THE VELOCITY of 17,545 miles per hour the atmosphere of the planet earth . . . is no longer an atmosphere. It is a great barrier reef of friction, a steel-hard ocean of fire. Atmosphere—even the most tenuous wisps of gas—does not mix well with velocity. The two are incompatible. When they meet, their reaction is violent. It becomes evident in the form of naked, searing heat.

To reach orbital speed and height, a capsule must be sent into space at great cost. That price is paid in the form of energy that is expended in prodigious quantities. It is visually clear in the golden flame that trails the Atlas booster for the Mercury spacecraft.

The 3,000-pound spacecraft in orbit, ghosting through space, represents the awesome kinetic energy expended by its booster in the form of many thousands of pounds of fuel and oxidizer transformed into howling fire.

Before that capsule may rest safely again on the surface of the earth, it must cast off the equivalent of the energy that carried it out into space. The price of fire is—fire.

When the capsule returns with its tremendous velocity into the atmosphere, the result is friction. The result of sustained, terrible friction is enormous quantities of heat.

That is the barrier reef of re-entry—and for Mercury-Atlas 6 it was necessary for John Glenn to traverse that barrier.

The journey demands precision. The capsule must be slowed in its orbital speed by just so many miles per hour. Its force of deceleration must be exact, and it must be aligned exactly in

Mercury capsule in orbital config-
uration

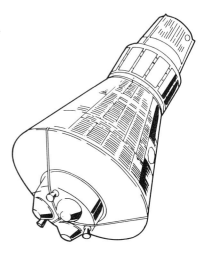

terms of the attitude of the capsule. The attitude of the capsule, once again, must be exact in relation to its course of flight as it first brushes, then prods gently, and finally plunges headlong into the atmosphere about our world.

An error during this descent can result in a reaction that comes with explosive speed and volcanic violence. A small error is compounded by the awesome forces at play into fiery catastrophe.

On the heat-shield end of the capsule are knobbed projections. There are six of these. Three contain the posigrade rockets that separate the capsule from the spent Atlas booster immediately after insertion into orbit. The other three are the retrorockets—to break the fine balance in gravity and centrifugal force that keeps the capsule in orbit, and to commence its return to earth.

Coming around near the end of its third orbit, the Mercury spacecraft is aligned with its longitudinal axis directly along the path of flight. It is tilted—the retropack faces up with an angle of exactly 34 degrees above the horizontal. As the capsule approaches the western coast of the United States, the timer in the capsule flashes its command to the retropack.

Each of the three rockets has a burning time of ten seconds; each fires with a thrust of 1,050 pounds. Retro One fires; five seconds later the second rocket blazes and, after another five seconds, the third ignites. It is a ripple fire. The burning of these

rockets exactly as planned is a *component of force*. This is designed to slow down the capsule by some 350 miles per hour.

No longer does the capsule have its circular—or, in reality,
its elliptical—path about the earth. Instead, it begins to fall in a
steeper arc that has become a greatly flattened ballistic trajectory. The end of that trajectory, calculated even without atmosphere, will rest on the surface of the earth.

The capsule falls, a timer fires explosive bolts. Metal straps
that clasp the retropack to the capsule spring free. As the
capsule makes its tentative brushes with atmosphere—the aerothermodynamic border high above earth—the retropack slides
free.

The ablative heat shield of spun resin glass is now fully exposed. That heat shield is *everything;* it is life itself. It is protection against incineration.

The capsule begins its re-entry along a very flat angle—no
more than one and a half degrees below the horizontal. It dips
more and more into the atmosphere. Friction joins gravity in
clawing at the capsule to drag it from its course high above
earth.

Fifty-five miles high the capsule is into denser atmosphere.
It is air so naked and thin a man would die from explosive
decompression almost instantly. To the human being it is a
vacuum. To the capsule with its hurtling speed it is the first
edges of the barrier reef. Here begins the first significant heating because of friction.

The retrorockets fire to the west of California. By the time it
is over the eastern coast of the United States the capsule has
edged down to 55 miles.

It streaks downward. Twenty-five miles above the earth the
capsule is moving at 15,000 miles per hour. At this moment the
temperature on the heat shield is 3,000° Fahrenheit! This is the
peak. It will last for perhaps another two minutes.

But this is not the only heat. The plunge through the rapidly
thickening air creates ahead of the capsule heat shield a tremendous bow wave. This is, literally, a blazing shock wave. Its
temperature reaches, perhaps even exceeds, an unbelievable

11,000° F. This is heat greater than that on the surface of the sun. It is heat beyond comprehension.

But this heat does not touch, does not reach the capsule. The bow wave is ahead, up and over—but well away from—the capsule itself. Where the capsule is concerned, the greatest heat occurs along the heat shield. The tremendous temperatures cause a strange process to occur on the surface of the heat shield. The resin material does not *absorb* the heat, and that is its secret for the survival of the man. Instead, the surface of the shield begins to vaporize. The terrible heat swirls away in an ablation process—thousands of degrees of heat boiling away from the capsule.

The shield vaporizes part of its surface at 3,000° F. The resinous material at its edges actually *flows*. Some of it creeps around the edge of the heat shield and flows back along the external surface of the capsule, over the window. The resinous film in Glenn's flight almost prevented direct vision through the window of *Friendship 7* as Glenn descended, finally, beneath his great parachute.

But there is also terrible heat along the surface of the capsule. Around the capsule the re-entry process creates a boundary layer of heat of 2,000°F. The entire capsule glows a brilliant red, the very surface of the metal itself glowing so brightly it seems to blaze. The layer of ionized air covering the capsule is a scene of violence. Atoms are stripped of electrons. The ionization becomes an electrical shield; for several minutes it blanks out all communications to and from the capsule.

The reduction in speed and altitude is impressive. Friction begins to leap into being when the capsule is 55 miles high. Over a slant range—a distance across the surface of the earth—of 760 miles, the capsule drops down to only 12 miles. This is a journey that takes approximately 300 seconds to complete. In this time the capsule decelerates to only 270 miles per hour. The 300 seconds' approximate time of deceleration may be compared to the 301.4 seconds from liftoff to insertion into orbit.

The procedure now is what a Canaveral engineer calls "atmospheric descent in a sensible manner." Approximately four miles

Spacecraft landing bag in deployed position at water impact

above the earth a six-foot drogue parachute opens to stabilize the capsule. The spacecraft drops without the severe oscillations that Glenn reported during re-entry—they are now damped out by the effect of the chute. The capsule continues to decelerate. Two miles high, the main parachute spills out—a red-and-white canopy 63 feet in diameter. For a few moments it is held in reefed condition—the canopy is not fully open. The capsule again slows; reef cutters slice the lines, and the canopy blossoms out full.

At 20 miles per hour, its external surfaces still hot, the spacecraft descends toward the ocean. Beneath the capsule the heat shield has dropped down four feet. A rubberized bag with air holes is extended; this fills with air. When the capsule strikes the water (the parachute automatically cuts loose), the air is vented explosively from the landing bag—a pneumatic cushion to ease the impact of landing. Quickly the bag fills with four tons of water, and acts as a stabilization device to keep the capsule floating upright.

Until recovery—this is the end of the mission.

But it did not happen quite this way with the flight of John Glenn. While he was in orbit, the stations on the ground received a signal that the heat shield had come loose. If this were so, then the survival of John Glenn during that fiery return to the earth was impossible. Instead of re-entry, the mission of Mercury-Atlas 6 would have ended in a blazing streak of light through the heavens.

And death by fire to the man within that capsule.

The grim last three hours of the orbital mission of John Glenn —because of a tiny switch—is a story incredible in its events, and gripping in its telling.

William Hines, the Science Writer for the *Washington Evening Star,* researched with meticulous, painstaking care this amazing story. One of the great science reporters of this country, Hines' special report, I feel, stands unexcelled. I am grateful to my friend and associate, William Hines, and to the *Washington Evening Star* and the North American Newspaper Alliance for their permission to present Bill Hines' special report—"Segment 51."

✿   ✿   ✿

"Segment 51"

For three harrowing hours . . . the life of a man and the prestige of a Nation hung in doubt.

In this period—so brief yet so long—Astronaut John Glenn made the final two of his three earth orbits while his colleagues on the ground wondered whether they would be able to get him back. Had they failed, not only would a brave man have perished, but this country's stature in the Space Age would have suffered tremendously.

This is the story of *Friendship 7's* heat shield, told by the men most intimately involved. It is a story of suspense and high adventure on an unknown frontier, of incisive detective work and cold engineering logic, of steely calm under stress. It is an adventure story, told for the first time, that will have an enduring place in the annals of the early Space Age.

The three-hour crisis of the heat shield began at 11:20 A.M. on February 20, just as Glenn was passing over the east coast at the end of his first orbit. In a room in the building at Cape Canaveral housing Mercury Control, a technician named Bill Saunders was scanning a bank of 90 small meters, each of which gave some information on the state of affairs aloft.

Suddenly his eyes froze on a meter numbered 51. He spoke into a telephone that linked him with Mercury Flight Director Christopher Columbus ("Chris") Kraft and Astronaut Alan B.

Shepard, who was the Cape's voice contact with his fellow spaceman in orbit:

"I've got a valid signal on Segment 51."

In the main Mercury Control room, the ordered busyness of a flight day continued. A dozen or so scientists, technicians, and engineers sat at consoles where blinking lights told a host of fast-paced tales. Across the front of the room was spread a map of the world, a capsule-shaped dot moving across its surface as *Friendship 7* moved through space. To the left and right of the map were banks of charts showing, minute by minute, the conditions of the astronaut and the major elements of his spacecraft.

Shepard was the first to react to Saunders' news. Kraft was for the moment occupied with the immediate flight situation. The ground communicator jotted down "Segment 51" and then did a double take. His heart skipped a beat. A signal on Segment 51, if accurate, meant that *Friendship 7's* heat shield had come loose while the spacecraft was still in orbit . . . that the shield had come loose in outer space, and was hanging in landing position. If that were true, things couldn't be worse.

The reading on Segment 51 didn't make sense to Shepard, and it didn't make sense to Chris Kraft, either. Neither man could see any way for the heat shield to come loose if the retrorocket package, which was mounted on it, was still in place. And conversely, if the rockets were not in place, the question of Glenn's re-entry was probably academic, anyway, because the "retros" were needed to slow him down from orbital speed so he could come back to earth.

These retrorockets sit in a round aluminum container called a retropack on the outside of the heat shield. The pack is held firmly to the capsule itself—not to the heat shield—by three stout straps of the exceedingly strong metal titanium. In effect, these straps serve to anchor the heat shield to the capsule as long as the retropack is on.

So reason said the retropack must go before the heat shield could drop loose, and all indications were that the pack was still in place with its rockets still unfired.

But still, there was that signal on Segment 51. . . .

(Above) *Alan Shepard reflects mounting tension in Mercury Control.* (Below) *Doctors in Mercury Control as they monitor Glenn's physical condition during his orbit.*

Kraft pondered the signal's signficance, trying to convince himself that it was false. He asked Saunders to report the signal strength, and Saunders replied, "Eighty per cent."

Far from dispelling his fears, this news sobered Kraft further. He knew that if everything was well, Segment 51 should be reading about ten per cent. What were the alternatives? Zero per cent might mean a bad meter; 100 per cent would mean a grounded circuit; 40 or even 50 per cent might mean a dirty switch. But 80? Eighty per cent should mean only one thing: the heat shield was loose.

Meanwhile the minutes were ticking away, each of them bringing John Glenn 295 miles closer to the point in space where the retrorockets would have to be fired for re-entry.

Somehow, the men of Mercury had to get to the bottom of the matter. And it wouldn't be easy, because the signal from Segment 51 was an obscure one that would have to be looked for in ground-station records all around the world. The alert was sent out: "Report on Segment 51."

Within minutes the word came back—a chilling word that confirmed Bill Saunders' original indication. The records of the other stations indicated the heat shield was indeed loose.

Hardly three-quarters of an hour had passed since the trouble had been spotted. On Shepard's recommendation Kraft withheld word of the difficulty from Glenn. "Chris agreed that we would not discuss it with John until we had a better handle on it," Shepard said later.

To get this "better handle," Kraft started calling in the experts. One of the first called was Bill Bland, a key man in the Mercury setup. He asked Bland to get with Kenneth Kleinknecht, the newly named Mercury project manager, and try to figure out what to do.

Kleinknecht and Bland retired to a small room near Saunders' cubicle and started gathering other experts—John Yardley and Ed Nieman from the McDonnell Aircraft Company, which built the capsule. And meantime, at a console in front of Kraft, Shepard and Systems Monitor Don Arabian were going over blueprints and wiring diagrams trying to locate a possible bug

in the circuitry. They were soon joined by Astronaut Donald
"Deke" Slayton.

The front-room huddle over, Slayton joined the back-roomers
to give a first-impression report. He, Arabian, and Shepard had
a strong suspicion that a small limit switch was giving a false
indication. If this interpretation was correct, there was nothing
wrong with the capsule after all.

Still, they couldn't be sure. . . .

Glenn remained in the dark about the trouble through the
early period. Finally, he recalls, Kraft asked him whether he had
any light indication on the capsule's "Landing Bag–Deploy"
switch, which would show if the landing bag had opened. This
was about halfway through the second orbit. It was, Glenn said
later, "the first I knew that anything was amiss. . . .

"From this question about whether I had a light indication,
I gathered that they probably had an indication on the ground
that all was not well in the capsule," Glenn added. From then
on, he kept one ear cocked for any suspicious noises behind him
that might indicate the heat shield was loose. Like the others,
he could not see how it could be loose, but it had to be considered as a possibility.

"This was of some concern, but I didn't sit and stew about it,
or worry about it at all," he said. "There wasn't anything I could
do about it if it had come loose."

In the back room, the experts took the problem apart with
engineering precision. They asked themselves what could be the
worst possible eventuality—from a practical point of view—and
how best to cope with it. As a starting point they assumed that
the heat shield had somehow become unlatched—but for the
present was being held in place by the titanium straps of the
retropack.

From this assumption they derived certain comfort: as long as
the straps held, the heat shield could not go anywhere. The
latching system around the bottom of the spacecraft was arranged so that the shield had to drop a full four-fifths inch
before it could come completely loose—and there wasn't four-
fifths inch of play in the straps.

But still, the heat shield had not been designed to re-enter the atmosphere at 17,000 miles an hour with a retropack on, and this had not been tried on any of the Mercury test flights or in a wind tunnel.

The big selling point for the heat shield had always been that its clean, spherical surface could dissipate heat away from the capsule by literally boiling itself away. What would happen when this smooth face was marred by the retropack—a lump the size and shape of a bushel basket?

The men in the back room struggled with the problem as far as they could on their own and then called in the man who had conceived the Mercury capsule's shape. This man, Maxime Faget, was in Houston, Texas. Consulted by phone, he said that his theoretical studies clearly indicated that the shield could survive re-entry with the retropack still attached. Theoreticians at the McDonnell plant in St. Louis, Missouri, where *Friendship 7* was made, were similarly reassuring.

By now a complete orbit of the earth, and more, had transpired, and Glenn was coming up over the Pacific toward Hawaii on his last pass before re-entry. Kraft, who (next to Glenn) was in the hottest seat of all, began to chafe for advice on which to base a decision. He had only a very few minutes left before he had to order firing of the retrorockets, ready or not, because there was no provision to keep Glenn up for another 90-minute orbit.

Shepard, Arabian, and Slayton had been over the wiring diagrams until their eyes burned. They were virtually certain that a switch was lying, but they couldn't guarantee it.

Bland, Yardley, and the others in the back room had come to the same conclusion. As they saw it, in the capsule there was a pesky little rotary switch, hardly bigger than a spool of thread, that was causing all the confusion. They reasoned that the shaft of the switch would have to rotate a full 60 degrees in the right direction to give a "Landing Bag–Deploy" signal, but only about one or two degrees in the wrong direction. And in such a little switch there could easily be one or two degrees of play in a rotating shaft no thicker than a lead pencil. But they couldn't guarantee that their theorizing was correct.

Kraft, a normally imperturbable man in his mid-thirties, felt tension growing within him. "I couldn't get a decision out of our back-room people," he recalled later. "I kept harassing them, and I couldn't get anything out of them. So I said, 'Either you guys are going to give a decision in five minutes or I am going to make one myself. I have no choice.'"

In the final minutes Kraft's advisers struggled through this line of reasoning:

To ignore the signal and take a chance that everything was all right would be a blind, unjustified risk. This alternative should be eliminated from further consideration.

This left the assumption that the signal was telling the truth. Now: Would it be better to re-enter normally without the retropack on and take a chance of the heat shield dropping prematurely? Or would it be better to re-enter with the retropack on and take a chance of overheating the capsule by interfering with the operation of the heat shield?

This finally brought the proper recommendation into focus. They knew that if the heat shield dropped off before re-entry Glenn would burn to death. They had reason to believe he could survive a re-entry with the retropack attached as long as the heat shield stayed in place. The men in the back room nodded to one another and sent John Yardley out to give Kraft their recommendation.

Meanwhile, the flight director took some preliminary action of his own. He told Hawaii to have Glenn flick on an indicating —not an actuating—switch marked "Landing Bag–Deploy," and report whether a light came on.

There were three possible reports Glenn could give: green, red, or no light. Green would mean that the heat shield had dropped off the capsule; red would mean it had disengaged but had not actually separated to form the landing bag; and no light would mean nothing had happened.

Of course—no light could also mean that the bulb had burned out. You couldn't be sure. . . .

Glenn reported no light on the switch indicator. So far so good.

"Yardley came out and explained the diagram to me in the same light that we had looked at them," Kraft recalled. "He described what he thought about holding the shield on with the straps, and he said the consensus of everybody was that the safest way to re-enter was with the package on."

Kraft looked across at the bland, round face of his boss, Manned Flight Operations Chief Walt Williams. The two of them knew what had to be done, and tried not to think about the Congressmen and other VIPs behind the glass in the viewing gallery who would be transformed suddenly into second-guessers if anything went wrong.

"When we finally made the decision we were already in contact with California, initiating the retrofire maneuver," Kraft recalled. From then on, things happened literally faster than they can be retold.

Kraft called Astronaut Walter Schirra, the capsule communicator at bleak Point Arguello on the coast northwest of Los Angeles. "California," he said, "I want you to tell him to keep his retro-jettison in the disarm position."

This meant that an automatic sequence in the re-entry maneuver would be interrupted before the retropack could be kicked off the face of the heat shield.

Schirra flashed the unusual instruction to Glenn, who says he immediately associated the recommendation with the earlier request for switch-light indications. Because the order was highly out of the ordinary, "I asked Wally the reason for it at the time," Glenn recalls. But by now, Glenn's speeding capsule was passing out of range of California, and Schirra was able only to say that the astronaut would get further instructions from Texas.

It was only at this point that radio and TV followers of the Mercury flight got their first inkling of this particular difficulty. As a matter of fact, only a sharp-eared and knowledgeable few knew enough about the Mercury program to raise an eyebrow when the "Voice of Mercury," Lt. Colonel John Powers, announced that re-entry with the retropack had been ordered.

As to why "Shorty" Powers had said nothing about the heat-shield problem before, all evidence points to the probability that he knew nothing about it. The powwows that had taken place had occurred quietly among a handful of specialists; probably not one man in five in Mercury Control knew at the time it was happening of the serious problem at hand.

Powers announced to the world that Glenn had been instructed to leave the retropack on until over Texas. This had been Schirra's original advice to the astronaut. But when *Friendship 7* came within range of Corpus Christi, Texas, capsule communicator George Guthrie had a later decision for him:

"We are recommending that you leave the retropackage on through the entire re-entry.

". . . Do you read me?"

"What is the reason for this? Do you have any reason?" Glenn asked.

"Not at this time. This is the judgment of Cape Flight," Guthrie replied. The explanation, he said, would come from Shepard at Mercury Control when *Friendship 7* got within range of the Cape.

When next Glenn spoke, his voice—as heard on tape-recorded playbacks—sounded just as level and calm as in normal conversation. "Ah, roger. This is *Friendship 7,* going to re-entry attitude in that case."

Commenting later, the spaceman said, "The die was cast, so to speak, at that point, anyway."

Friendship 7 was streaking across the southern tier of the United States by this time, its retrorockets already fired, the empty retropack still on the forward end of the capsule. Glenn still had an explanation coming to him. In due course it came, from Al Shepard at the Cape:

"We are not sure whether or not your landing bucket has deployed. We feel that it is far safer to re-enter with the retropackage on. We see no difficulty at this time in that type of re-entry. Over."

As calmly as if he was bringing a DC-3 in for a daylight landing on Runway 36, John Glenn said:

"Ah, roger. Understand."

There was little time for chitchat. Ahead of Glenn was an inevitable—and quite precisely measurable—period of time when he would lose radio contact with the earth. Flight planners

Mercury capsule re-entering with retropack on

had estimated this "blackout" or communications-loss period would last four minutes and 23 seconds; it turned out to last 4:22. But during this period John Glenn was by all odds the loneliest man in the world.

Just before communications were lost, an afterthought was beamed to him by Shepard: Dump the retropack when the deceleration meters show between 1 and 1.5g. This would be just a safety step, not really essential. As it happened, the first words: "Recommend that—" got through, but the recommendation never did.

Then ensued a bad four minutes. "It seemed like a day," Kenny Kleinknecht said later.

Everyone on the ground was lost in his own thoughts, knowing that everything possible had been done . . . and that if anything had been done wrong it could not be undone.

Inside *Friendship 7* the man with the most to lose lived his moment of truth. At his homecoming in New Concord, Ohio, he was later to answer a question about "his finest hour" by saying, "I guess it was when I came through re-entry in real good shape."

Somewhere quite early in re-entry deceleration one of the

three titanium straps on the retropack let go, and the loose end of it could be seen through the capsule window. At about the same time, he felt a considerable bump behind him.

"I assumed that this was the retropack being jettisoned," Glenn said later. "I thought at the time that it had left the capsule and we had a clean heat shield for re-entry. I still had no landing-bag indication; I checked it at that time, so I thought the heat shield was probably in real good shape."

What followed immediately was probably the roughest period of all for Glenn. His recollection:

"We came along into the higher part of the heat pulse. There was an orange glow outside the capsule. And at that point I started seeing sparks and small pieces coming back, flaming.

"And then there were some fairly large chunks of six or seven inches across, possibly, that were flaming. I wasn't sure what had happened, because I felt that earlier the retropack had jettisoned. I wasn't sure but that we might in some way have damaged the heat shield—perhaps it might be tearing up."

Glenn could not even hope for an immediate answer to his unspoken question: Had the heat shield gone? The way *Friendship 7* was built, the damage would be done first, and the heat would get in later—if heat was going to get in. There was nothing to do but wait, control the capsule's vibrations as well as he could, and try to re-establish contact with the ground. And all this while he knew that if the heat shield had disintegrated he could not possibly survive.

"This is *Friendship 7*, do you read me? Over." Time and again through this harrowing period he asked this question. Even at the peak of his anxiety Glenn's voice—in playbacks of tape recordings made within the capsule—betrayed no loss of equanimity, although ever so slightly there was an added element of strain as the buildup of *g* forces made it physically difficult for him to talk.

Then, finally, just as suddenly as it had begun and right on schedule, the communications loss ended and Glenn's voice came through: "This is *Friendship 7*, do you read me? Over."

To most of the men on the ground the letdown of relief was as great as the buildup of tension had been. But not to Al Shepard, Glenn's predecessor in space.

"How do you feel?" Shepard asked Glenn.

"Oh, pretty good," the voice came back. But to Shepard it didn't sound "pretty good" at all. It sounded tense and strained.

"I thought maybe he'd taken too much heat," Shepard said later.

Glenn could not recall any feelings of discomfort. "I was in good shape then," he said. "I was quite elated at the time. We had been through the worst and everything was settling down. The glow had gone down. Everything was in good shape. All we had to do was get down and get the parachutes out and then we'd have it made."

Perhaps, Glenn said, the apparent strain in his voice was due to the fact that he was still under pretty high decelerative forces, and was attempting to talk between deep-breathing exercises designed "to spread the lungs out again."

Finally the parachutes opened, and the capsule was recovered, and the rest is history.

What caused the trouble? As the men in Mercury Control had suspected, a little shaft in a tiny limit switch had rotated a hairsbreadth in the wrong direction.

With the added benefit of hindsight, the men who participated in the decision say now that John Glenn was not in mortal danger at all. But they quickly add that if they had to do it over again, they would undoubtedly go through the same route. As it turned out, the heat shield was on firmly all the time, and they could have made a completely normal re-entry with no risk at all.

But still, there was that 80-per-cent reading on Segment 51. As Al Shepard said later: "We couldn't be sure."

❀   ❀   ❀

On February 23, at his post-flight press conference held at Cape Canaveral, Colonel Glenn remarked:

This is what can happen when things go wrong. . . . This Mercury capsule was fired in July of 1960. The booster exploded one minute after launch. The capsule was not equipped in this test with its escape system; it struck the water on its side at 400 mph ten miles off Canaveral. Engineers pieced this partial wreckage together.

"As it [the capsule] went into the higher heat belt this glow picked up outside the capsule to sort of a bright orange glow outside the window.

"It became apparent that something was tearing up on the heat shield end of the capsule because there were large pieces as big as the end of your finger to pieces probably seven to eight inches in diameter . . . were breaking off and falling off the edge of the capsule and coming back up the window and were flaming very brightly.

"You could see the fire and the glow from them as they would come up back past the window.

"Well, this, obviously, was the retro package tearing up and breaking off as we knew it would if it had been retained. I thought at that time, however, that the retro package had already been jettisoned.

"So there were some moments of doubt there as to whether the heat shield had been damaged and whether it might be tearing up itself.

"And this could have been a bad day all the way around if that had been the case. . . . "

Recovering capsule by ship

VIII: *The Orbital Flights of the Soviet Cosmonauts*

THE AGE OF SPACE on April 12, 1961, entered a new era. On that day, for the first time, man no longer was an observer from the ground of the miracle of flight through space. From a distance of more than 200 miles above the surface of his world, a man named Yuri Alekseyevich Gagarin looked down. Later, he said: "I saw for the first time with my eyes the earth's spherical shape. You can see its curvature when looking to the horizon.

" . . . the view of the horizon is quite unique and very beautiful. It is possible to see the remarkably colorful change from the light surface of the earth to the completely black sky in which one can see the stars.

"This dividing line is very thin, just like a belt of film surrounding the earth's sphere, a film like a narrow belt girdling the globe. It is of a soft light blue color and the entire transition from blue to black is most smooth and beautiful. . . .

"When I emerged from the earth shadow, the horizon seemed different. It had a bright orange strip which then resolved itself into blue and again into pitch black.

" . . . The sun in outer space is tens of times brighter than here on earth. The stars are visible very well. They are bright and distinct. The entire picture of the firmament presents much more contrast than when seen from the earth.

"The day side of the earth was clearly visible. The coasts of continents, islands, big rivers, big surfaces of water, and structural features were clearly distinguishable.

" . . . The appearance of the earth's surface is roughly the

Vostok *spaceship with protective nose fairing installed, and tail annulus for circular airfoil manned control by pilot in atmosphere.*

same as we can see in flights to great heights in jet aircraft. It is very good.

"Large mountain areas, large rivers and forests, the coastline, islands were easily distinguishable. During the space flight I was fully able to adhere to what we pilots call navigation by geographical locality. The clouds covering the surface of the earth could be seen very well, the shadows of these clouds on the earth. The sky, however, was quite black. . . .

"The earth has a very characteristic and very beautiful blue halo. The aureole becomes distinct at the horizon when gradual transition in colors takes place from soft blue light, from light blue to blue, dark blue, violet to black, to a quite black sky. . . . When emerging from the shadow [of the earth] the sun fell on and penetrated the atmosphere and here this halo took on a slightly different color.

"On the surface itself, on the very horizon of the surface, one could see a bright orange color, which then merged into all the colors of the rainbow, giving light blue, deep blue, violet and black colors to the sky.

"The entry into the earth's shadow comes very quickly. Darkness comes at once and nothing is visible. At this time on the surface I saw nothing was visible, since, obviously, I was passing over the ocean. . . .

"The emergence from the earth's shadow also occurs very quickly and abruptly. . . . "

These descriptions of earth and space through the eyes of

a man were spoken ten months before Astronaut John Glenn shot into his three orbits of the earth in a Mercury capsule. On April 12, 1961, Yuri Alekseyevich Gagarin was sent into orbit atop a giant Russian rocket booster.

Long minutes later, when the upper stage of the carrier rocket exhausted its fuel and shut down, Gagarin and his spaceship *Vostok I* were in orbit with a velocity of approximately 18,000 miles per hour.

The orbital parameters of the first manned space flight provide an interesting comparison with those of John Glenn's mission (and incidentally also those of Scott Carpenter, whose orbital parameters were almost identical with Glenn's). Glenn orbited from 100 miles at his lowest point to 162 miles at apogee, and during this orbit his greatest velocity was 17,545 miles per hour.

It is surprising to note that in the first manned orbital flight ever made, Gagarin reached a speed and height that at this writing still have not been exceeded. *Vostok I* orbited from a low point (perigee, or closest approach to earth in orbit) of 112.47 miles. As the Russian spaceship looped around the planet, it lofted to a high point of 203.19 miles, much higher than that achieved by either Glenn or Carpenter—or the succeeding flights of Titov, Nikolayev, and Popovich.

We do not know the exact details of the Russian booster rocket as we know intimately the details and characteristics of Atlas 109-D. While the Russians have released a great amount of detail on the actual spaceship, they have chosen to remain virtually silent in respect to their booster rocket. It is a modified intercontinental ballistic missile; that much is certain. It has two stages, and in their dossier submitted to the FAI (Federation Aeronautique Internationale), the world body which certifies official space-flight records (both the United States and the USSR are members), the Russians revealed that the spacecraft booster had a total of six engines. It developed a thrust which the Russians submitted in kilograms—and converts to a maximum usable thrust of 1,323,000 pounds, which is some four times greater than that of Atlas 109-D.

The size of *Vostok I*—even after all this time—is staggering.

The spaceship weighed 10,416 pounds (this is the record pay-load weight for a manned vehicle ever placed in orbit, as certified by FAI). More than 20 feet long and approximately 12 to 14 feet in diameter, this first Russian ship was a giant in comparison to the Mercury capsule.

Gagarin's flight was a "test mission"—a proving flight of one orbit only. The orbital period of the spaceship was 89.1 minutes; the total time spent for the mission from liftoff to return to the land surface of the earth was 108 minutes.

Launch site was from the cosmodrome at Baikonur; landing area, near Krasney Koot, in the Saratov region of the USSR.

Some other comparisons are interesting. The Mercury capsule weighed 2,987 pounds in orbit, 7,429 pounds less than *Vostok I*. The Atlas 109-D booster weighed approximately 10,000 pounds in its orbital configuration. I asked Mercury officials how many times 109-D orbited the earth; they replied that the booster was not tracked in orbit, but that "it is unlikely that it would make more than one or two orbits before entry into the atmosphere."

Atlas 109-D went into orbit at 100 miles, but the perigee of the Russian booster was 112.47 miles. The decreased resistance at the edges of the aerothermodynamic border enabled the massive rocket to orbit for four days before re-entering the atmosphere.

Training the Cosmonauts

The Russian man-in-space program was an accomplished fact late in 1957, nearly one year prior to the activation of Project Mercury in the United States—an advantage that the USSR pressed hard in the following years. Contrary to the belief widely held in the United States (a "natural" conclusion drawn because of a lack of knowledge of the Russian program for many months), the Russian cosmonauts were not test pilots, as are the astronauts in this country. Instead, Soviet Air Force officers visited those men considered most promising for space flight, throughout the entire Air Force, and offered them the chance to volunteer for "hazardous and special duty."

Several hundred pilots—from all segments of the Air Force—reported under the strictest secrecy to a major medical center near Moscow. The men were here for several weeks. Doctors subjected them to exhaustive physical and psychological examinations, much the same as those taken by our astronauts. The process "weeded out" the least fit; this is an unfair label, both for the cosmonauts and our astronauts. What is the "least fit" among a select group of prospective spacemen is a brilliant standout among most men.

The initial series of tests separated for more extensive training and processing 50 pilots. These men reported to a training camp that at first dismayed them. Where they had expected to see a vast and supermodern center of enormous hangars, great gantries, and towering rockets—and all the signs of a sprawling technological establishment—they found themselves instead at an ordinary military training camp for soldiers that was no different from a thousand other such camps throughout the USSR. The barracks were wooden, long, and austere. The camp had the usual facilities of a messhall, classrooms (although these were little used at this point of training), and above all, it had what the cosmonauts described as "superb physical-conditioning equipment." Gherman S. Titov, in fact, stated that the gymnasium at the camp was the "finest I had ever seen, anywhere in the country."

For several months the 50 cosmonauts were run through the physical-conditioning mill. As pilots they were in good condition to begin with; as cosmonauts they had to be as perfect as it was possible to achieve in terms of physical tone, strength, co-ordination, body rhythm, and other characteristics. The cosmonauts time and again ran through obstacle courses, played fiercely competitive sports, and did hour upon hour of calisthenics. Slowly their numbers were depleted as the physical conditioning took its toll, as the Russian doctors raised higher their minimum standards. When they were through, only 12

(Above) *Cosmonaut Yuri A. Gagarin during parachute training activities in 1958.* (Below) *With biosensors taped to his body, Gherman S. Titov is prepared for centrifuge test under high g loads.*

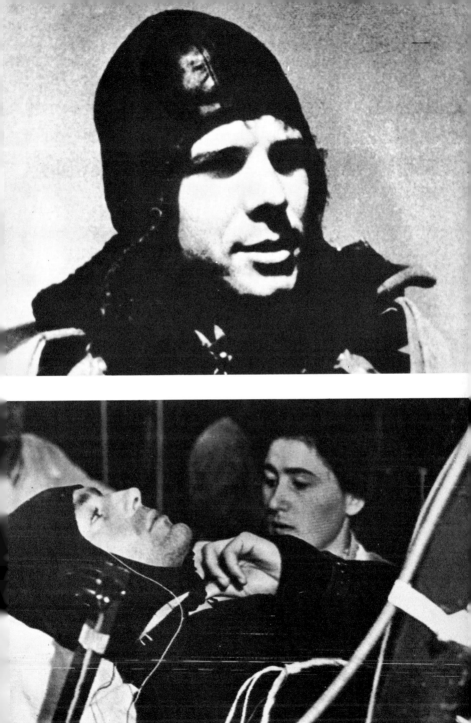

remained—the 12 cosmonauts who then began the intensive advanced training for space flight.

Among the major differences in the Russian training program from that of Project Mercury is the concentration in the USSR upon parachute training and jumping. The cosmonauts made more than 40 jumps each during their final training in the field. Titov explains that their instructor was a world record holder, the finest in the USSR. They jumped, Titov and Gagarin both have stated, in all kinds of weather and under all conditions—from transports and small airplanes, and even ejections from jet aircraft. They jumped over level and rough country, in daylight and at night, and in calm air and under high winds.

Yuri Gagarin had had only three years as a pilot before his selection as a cosmonaut; he was a senior lieutenant in the Red Air Force when he volunteered for space-flight training. Gherman Titov was assigned to a jet supersonic combat fighter group near Leningrad. Most of the other cosmonauts, like Nikola-yev and Popovich, it appears, also were fighter pilots.

Although these men did not have the extensive technical and engineering backgrounds of the American astronauts—they were not test pilots and they were on the average between seven and ten years younger than the Americans—they were selected for their extremely high intelligence. Their technical training program was long, and it was intensive. Before the cosmonauts completed the training, they were considered entirely capable in all the technical sciences, with many of their capabilities as fighter pilots forming a broad base upon which to build.

Since the study of the human body, its functions, its reactions to stimuli of all sorts, and above all its adaptability to different situations has been a major science in the USSR for decades, the Russians feel that they already enjoyed a major advantage over the United States in aeromedical science—in bioastronautics —when the Russian program began. Many of the top space scientists in the United States are fully in agreement with the Russian view in this area, and they are willing to concede to the USSR a time advantage at present of at least three years. The Russian life-support and environmental systems of their spaceships are considerably more advanced than our own, and it appears abundantly clear that they were working hard on medical space-flight studies while this area was largely ignored in our own country.

Although there are some technical differences, and there are different areas of emphasis, the training of the cosmonauts and the astronauts in respect to simulators and training aids seems much the same. The Russians performed extensive work in centrifuges, as did we. They built elaborate training devices which simulated every possible aspect of space flight capable of achievement on the surface of the earth with a constant 1g force. And also like our own program, the Russians performed extensive zero gravity tests in both fighter airplanes and transports, in which weightlessness is achieved for periods up to 60 seconds. In these programs an airplane dives to a high speed; the pilot pulls up and enters a precise arc through the sky—a parabola. For a major portion of this arc the airplane is neatly balanced out between gravity and centrifugal force, and its occupants are just as weightless as they would be in orbit about the earth.

Vostok I

By any standards of measurement, the Russian spaceship flown by Gagarin is huge when compared to the spacecraft of Project Mercury. An immediately noticeable difference, other than size and shape (*Vostok* was more of a thick cylinder than a bell-shaped capsule), is the absence of the escape tower and rocket in the Russian spacecraft. Instead of employing this system, the Russians took advantage of the size and weight of *Vostok I* to equip Gagarin with a heavy seat. This contained not only many of the life-supporting systems for his flight, but it also carried an extensive arrangement of survival equipment and supplies should Gagarin come down to earth at sea, or in a remote area of the earth's surface. But more than this, the seat partially encloses the cosmonaut. It is mounted on heavy supporting guide rails, and is equipped with a powerful rocket-

(Above) *Gherman Titov in spacesuit enters training simulator in major cosmonaut training center outside Moscow.* (Below) *The* Vostok I *spaceship flown by Gagarin on April 12, 1961, for the world's first orbital flight. The spacecraft is about 12 to 14 feet wide and more than 22 feet in length. The official record (international) lists the weight of Vostok I in orbit at 10,416.84 pounds.*

explosive charge. It is, in other words, a complete ejection seat similar to those found in the most modern jet-fighter and bomber aircraft. It provides protection to its occupant against windblast, is stabilized to prevent any wild tumbling or other motions, and contains automatic equipment to separate the pilot from his seat; this equipment also opens the pilot's parachute and activates part of his survival-gear equipment. Systems similar to these are found in our military aircraft—but not yet in our spacecraft.

In an emergency, the cosmonaut would be blasted free of his spaceship directly in his seat. Even were he unconscious, the automatic systems would activate the landing sequences.

(It is a system with a great deal to say for it. The two-man Gemini space capsule now under construction and test by the United States follows to a great extent this pattern of design and function. Gemini will not have an escape tower or rocket; both pilots will be protected through the ejection-seat system.)

We have already described in great detail the equipment and the environment maintained with the Mercury *Friendship 7* spacecraft. Comparisons made with the *Vostok* provide an indication of how the Russians exploited to the full their advantages of size and volume.

Gagarin's contour couch—part of his seat and not a fixed part of his ship, as is the couch of the Mercury capsule—was mounted on bearings, states a Russian report, so that it could shift its position within the spacecraft. This permitted the cosmonaut, in unusual ship maneuvers, to be always horizontal across the line of travel. In this position he could best bear the pressure of accelerative forces.

Gagarin had three viewports for direct visual observations in space—both for viewing and for navigational and attitude-control orientation in orbit. The ports were made of heavy, heat-resistant glass with special metal shields. These could be operated through pilot remote control from his couch or kept on automatic control, the shutters sliding into place during the fierce heat of re-entry.

At the base of the spaceship was a compartment with an

extensive array of special instruments. There was a major interior compartment and a second smaller cabin. To enter the spacecraft the cosmonaut simply stooped down and climbed in —unlike the cautious wriggle into the Mercury capsule that our astronauts must perform. To close the hatch of *Vostok*, Gagarin simply reached out to his control panel and closed a switch; the heavy door closed electrically and was automatically sealed, and locked. The closing of the hatch in the Mercury capsule is a laborious and time-consuming process; many engineers state that it is not necessary to have this system, that improved hatch designs will be used in our next spacecraft series.

In *Vostok I*, Gagarin flew with a cabin pressure of some 15 pounds per square inch—just above sea-level normal. Oxygen pressure and concentration were maintained at sea-level conditions, and an elaborate life-environment system kept carbon-dioxide concentration to less than 1.0 per cent, temperature from 60° to 75° F. (*Friendship 7* reached much higher temperatures), and the relative humidity from 30 to 70 per cent. "Highly active chemical compounds" were used in the atmospheric regeneration system, linked to sensors and controls that maintained the desired pressure and concentrations of oxygen and carbon dioxide. In the same fashion, humidity was controlled with "special filters" to "purify the air by removing harmful impurities that are thrown off by the human organism and by the machinery." A Russian scientist added that "the reserves of food, water, recovered substances, and the capacity of the electrical power sources are calculated for a flight lasting up to ten days."

On the spaceship's external surface was a solar heat exchanger containing a system of shutters that closed or opened for exposure to solar radiation as temperature demands within the spaceship varied. Within *Vostok I* was an automatic thermo-regulating system with a "liquid cooling agent," in which the liquid flowed into a liquid-pneumatic radiator, automatically controlling the flow of air within the radiator.

The Flight of Vostok I

The flight of *Vostok I* with Major Yuri Gagarin began at seven minutes past nine o'clock the morning of April 12, 1961. For a time period that is best calculated at approximately 300 seconds the two-stage rocket fired toward the desired orbital altitude, attitude, and velocity. The flight was much more sharply inclined to the equator than with the American orbital flights; Gagarin's orbit was inclined 64 degrees 57 minutes to the equator, in comparison to the inclination for Glenn of 32.5 degrees. Because of this steeper inclination, Gagarin passed over a greater area of earth (and Titov in *Vostok II* would pass over most of the earth's surface during his 17 orbits).

As he ascended, Gagarin reported that he turned his head slightly to look through a viewport: "I see the earth in haze. . . . My, it is beautiful."

Finally, the second stage of the booster was exactly in the position planned. The power was cut abruptly; the heavy spaceship eased away from its inert carrier rocket, and began its turnaround to re-entry attitude. Gagarin's first words, the first ever spoken from space, were:

"*Ya kharashom nastroyeniyii. Machina rabotayet kharasho.* . . . I am in good spirits. The machine works perfectly. . . ."

Gagarin's reactions to weightlessness were better than the Soviet doctors had dared to hope:

"Once I was in orbit, once I was separated from the carrier rocket, I experienced weightlessness. At first this sensation was somewhat unusual, even though I had experienced it before for short periods. But I quickly became accustomed to this sensation of weightlessness, adapted myself to this situation, and continued to carry out the program which was set to me during the flight.

". . . During the orbital flight I took food and drank water, I maintained constant radio contact with the earth along several channels both on telephony and telegraphy signals. I made observations of the conditions of my environment, of the functioning of the equipment of the spaceship. I made reports back to earth, made entries of these observations in my logbook, and recorded them on a tape recorder.

"My feelings during the entire period of weightlessness were excellent and my capacity for work was fully maintained.

"It became easier to do everything when [I] became weightless. This was quite natural. One's legs, arms weigh nothing. Objects float in the cabin. Neither did I myself sit in the chair as I did before that, but hung in midair."

Within 15 minutes of the launching of *Vostok I*, American radar stations had fed data into our air defense warning computers, and tracking reports were already on their way to Washington. Fifty-three minutes after the moment of launch (ten a.m. Moscow Time) the Soviets announced to the world the orbital flight of Yuri Gagarin (Dr. Jerome Weisner had already given detailed reports of the flight by this time to the President).

As the ship raced from daylight into darkness and then into daylight again, a solar orientation system clicked on. One axis of *Vostok* was aligned with the sun through optical and gyroscopic instruments. These transmitted signals to the control system which, in turn, "ordered" the control devices to stabilize the spaceship according to preflight plans.

Gagarin's instrumentation was minimal but fully adequate to the needs of the space mission. He watched a globe that was synchronized to rotate with the movement of *Vostok*. In the event of an in-flight emergency, Gagarin also watched an "optical orientator" mounted on a porthole, consisting of two circular mirror reflectors, a light filter, and a periscope with a grid.

If *Vostok* flew true and was properly oriented in its orbital parameters, Gagarin observed the horizon image in "the form of a ring in the field of vision." He studied the orientation of *Vostok* along its longitudinal axis by watching the "travel" of the earth's surface (the "drift" that Glenn refers to in his MA-6 flight), and had controls which would turn the spacecraft so that "the horizon line could be seen in the orientator in the form of a concentric ring, and the direction of 'travel' of the earth's surface would coincide with the course line of the grid."

As Gagarin raced around the planet, two television cameras monitored his flight. One showed a full-face view and the other a profile view. In his radio-telephone system was a magnetic recorder that taped his words in flight and then on command transmitted them to tracking/recording facilities on the surface.

Gagarin performed a series of tests—eating, drinking, writing in his log, working a telegraph key, voice recorder, operating radios, monitoring instruments, adjusting flight-timer controls— all this performed with the faceplate of his suit helmet open, a sign of tremendous confidence on the part of the Russians in the integrity of the spacecraft. As Gagarin stressed later in a press conference: "Everything was easy to perform. . . . Legs and arms weighed nothing. . . . Objects were swimming in the cabin. . . . I could have gone on forever."

Vostok became a time machine as Gagarin fled from Tuesday to Wednesday and back to Tuesday. At the southernmost part of his orbit he streaked past Antarctica, 2,000 miles below Santiago, Chile. He flashed past Cape Horn, raced through darkness, and swung back to his second dawn of the morning.

Then the Atlantic was below, and Russian technicians on the tracking ships passed their orientation reports to Gagarin.

". . . the sign was given for the descent. The ship was oriented in the proper way, the braking engine apparatus was switched on, and the speed reduced to what was necessary for the descent to earth. The descent took place as envisaged in the flight program. . . ."

At 10:35 a.m. Moscow Time Gagarin plunged through space over Central Africa, 120 miles above the surface of the planet. He was at this point 4,500 miles from the Saratov region of Russia. The retrofire timer clicked home. Two liquid-propellant rockets blazed in space, and the heavy *Vostok* began to decelerate in its rush around the earth. The rockets died out; the earth began to reclaim its own.

In its giant arc the spaceship plummeted with high precision toward the planned landing area. It glowed, then seemed to

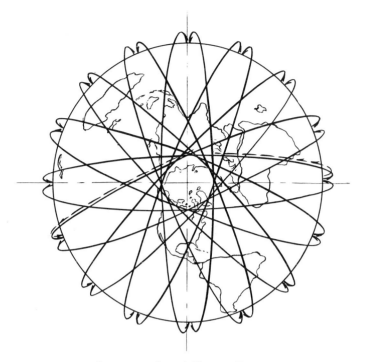

Seventeen orbits of Gherman Titov

burn with intense heat as friction scrubbed furiously along the metal skin. One hour and 48 minutes after the booster left the pad at Baikonur, Yuri Gagarin was again on the surface of the earth, standing in a farm field near Smedlovka, a village 400 miles southeast of Moscow.

The first manned orbital flight was at its successful end. Now the way was clear for the first sustained, manned, orbital *journey.*

The First Sustained Space Journey

By the time of the second Russian orbital manned flight—four months after the single pass about the planet by Gagarin—considerably more information was being obtained on the Russian spacecraft and supporting systems. We know now, for example, through records submitted by the USSR to the FAI, that the

Baikonur launch site (the cosmodrome) lies at 47 degrees 22 minutes North latitude, 65 degrees 25 minutes East longitude. The landing area at Krasney Koot in the Saratov region is at 50 degrees 51 minutes North latitude, 47 degrees 01.5 minutes East longitude. All four Russian manned orbital flights were launched from Baikonur, but Nikolayev and Popovich landed 373 miles east of Baikonur, near the town of Karaganda.

Gherman Stepanovich Titov began his space journey at nine o'clock the morning of August 6, 1961—and returned to earth 25 hours 18 minutes later, after orbiting the planet in just over 17 complete circuits. The exact (FAI record) weight for *Vostok I*, flown by Gagarin, is 10,416.84 pounds; the weight of *Vostok II* came to 10,408 pounds.

Statistical details on the flight show that the Titov orbit was considerably more circular than that for Gagarin, and slightly more circular than that for Glenn in *Friendship 7*. The perigee for *Vostok II* was 110.36 miles and the apogee 159.34 miles. Each orbital period was 88.46 minutes, compared to 89.1 minutes for Gagarin and 88.2 minutes for Glenn. The distance traveled for Titov is (FAI official records) 436,937.31 miles; that for Glenn is 83,450 miles.

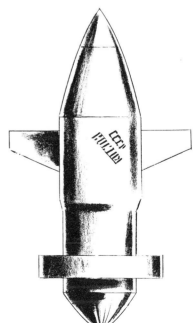

View of advanced five-ton Vostok *spaceship showing the tail annulus and circular airfoil, and stub wings for limited manned pilot control through atmosphere. Protective nose fairing is also installed.*

Statistical comparisons show three orbits for *Friendship 7*, just over 17 orbits for *Vostok II*. From beginning of the flight to landing, *Friendship 7* was "airborne" four hours 56 minutes. But the reader will notice a slight discrepancy in the records for *Vostok II*. Titov's flight lasted, from blastoff to his return to earth, for 25 hours 18 minutes. The official FAI records, however, show the flight's duration as 25 hours 11 minutes. The "lost seven minutes" stem from the evaluation of the flight as insisted upon to the FAI by the United States. On his return from space Titov ejected in his seat from *Vostok II* at an altitude of 21,325 feet. At this point his flight was 25 hours 11 minutes old; the U.S. insists that the space mission (for the records) ended the moment Titov ejected, and not when he landed by personal parachute—seven minutes later.

Just as the Mercury capsules embodied major improvements over the capsules previously flown in tests, so *Vostok II* incorporated modifications from Gagarin's spaceship. Both cosmo-

Cosmonaut seat from Vostok II spaceship, shown in readiness for ejection from Vostok. Titov grips two handles between his legs to help brace his body, and arm explosive ejection devices. He ejected from Vostok II at four miles altitude.

nauts have described the spacecraft interior as "much larger than anticipated, and quite unlike the interior of the familiar MIG fighters." The large contour couch dominates the cabin interior.

The official Russian description of this equipment:

> The pilot's seat incorporated a number of systems and devices that permitted the cosmonaut to live in the cabin for an extended period or, in case of need, to escape from the ship and land safely on earth. The seat could detach itself from the cabin automatically in the event of trouble on takeoff or on the powered leg of the flight. It carried a supply of oxygen and a ventilating device for the cosmonaut's pressurized suit. It also carried a radio receiver-transmitter, a supply of food and other vital articles that he might need for a forced landing. The supporting surfaces of the seat were upholstered with soft plastic cushions shaped to the human body. The parachute system contained in the seat allowed for a stabilized descent to the ground or water if the pilot had to leave the spaceship and land by parachute. If the landing had to be made on water, an automatically in-flated boat [raft] would have been ready for his use the instant he touched the surface.

> For added safety in a forced landing on water the spacesuit could keep the pilot afloat face upward. It was airtight and in-sulated so that the pilot could stay in water with a temperature of 32° F. for 12 hours without discomfort. The spacesuit was worn over woollen underwear. Under the spacesuit the pilot wore overalls. The glass faceplate in his helmet could be opened and closed both manually and automatically in the event the pressure or composition of the air in the cabin changed beyond safe limits. The spacesuit and the systems contained in it would have made it possible for the cosmonaut to control the ship even had the cabin lost its airtightness.

> The ship's air-conditioning and pressure-regulating equipment automatically kept the air composition, humidity, and pressure at normal [i.e., sea-level pressure and composition]. In an emer-gency the pilot could take over the controls to raise or lower the temperature or humidity, or change the composition of the air. *Vostok II*'s air-regenerating unit was an improvement on *Vostok I*'s setup, chemical and design.

The specially prepared foods—juices, chocolate, pâtés, etc.—were packed in tubes. Water was carried in a tank and sipped through a mouthpiece and tube.

Gherman Titov in training . . . (above) *during technical study work and* (below) *practicing snorkel swimming techniques.*

In the capacious cabin were "three portholes and two snap-action manholes. The glass of the portholes was heat resistant so that the pilot could make observations while in orbit and on the downward leg of the flight. Each of the portholes had motor-driven curtains to shut out the sunlight, if necessary."

Vostok II was equipped with enough food, water, sanitation equipment, and electrical power sources to orbit for ten days and nights.

The spacecraft carried voice radio, telegraph, and television equipment; an autonomous system for recording the data accumulated by instruments; a complete physiological monitoring, recording, and telemetering system for the cosmonaut; a special radio system for orbital measurements; and combinations of these systems to meet emergency purposes. On the exterior surface of the spaceship were the reaction jets, orientation elements, shutters of the temperature-control system, and all communications systems aerials.

Greater details were available on the life-environment system of *Vostok II:*

> The air-conditioning system in the space vehicle maintains normal pressure and normal oxygen content, a carbon dioxide content of not more than one per cent, a temperature of $15-22°$ C., and a relative humidity of 30–70 per cent. Regeneration of the air—absorption of carbon dioxide and water vapor and injection of the necessary quantity of oxygen—is effected by means of highly active chemical compounds. The regeneration process is automatically controlled. If the amount of oxygen drops and the concentration of carbon dioxide increases, a special sensor gives a signal which alters the operation of the regenerator. If an excess of oxygen is produced a mechanism automatically reduces the amount of oxygen injected into the air of the cabin. The humidity of the air is controlled in a similar way.
>
> A system of special filters is designed to purify the air in case of contamination by harmful admixtures resulting from the functions of the pilot's body and the work of the instruments.
>
> The required temperature is maintained by a special temperature-control system. A specific feature of this system is the use of a constant-temperature liquid-cooling agent to transfer heat from the pilot's cabin. The cooling agent flows through the temperature-control system to a liquid-gas radiator. The flow of air

through the radiator is regulated automatically, depending on the temperature in the ascending vehicle. The required temperature is thus maintained with great accuracy.

More information was provided on the control system of the two *Vostoks*, which, apparently, remained unchanged in the two spacecraft:

In order to orientate the ship when steered manually the cosmonaut uses an optical orientation device to determine the position of the ship in relation to the earth. This optical device is installed in one of the portholes of the cabin. It consists of two annular mirror reflectors, a light filter, and a latticed glass. The rays traveling from the line of the horizon strike the first reflector and, passing through the glass of the porthole, reach the second reflector, which directs them through the latticed glass to the eyes of the cosmonaut. If the ship's bearings in relation to the vertical axis are correct, the cosmonaut sees the horizon in the form of a circle in his field of vision.

Through the central part of the porthole the cosmonaut sees the part of the earth's surface directly below him. The position of the ship's longitudinal axis in relation to the direction of flight is determined by watching the "run" of the earth's surface in the pilot's field of vision.

With the help of the control units the cosmonaut can turn the ship in a direction ensuring that the line of the horizon is visible in the orientation system in the form of a concentric circle, and that the direction of the earth's "run" coincides with the course plotted on the latticed glass (chart). This will be proof of the correct orientation of the ship. The pilot's field of vision can be covered by the light filter or shutter if necessary.

A globe installed on the instrument panel makes it possible, in addition to ascertaining the ship's bearing during the flight, to predetermine the landing place if the braking device is switched on at any moment during the mission. . . .

Gherman Titov refers specifically to his navigation equipment with a description of the "magnificent colored globe of the planet that would rotate in unison with the oceans and continents . . . under my spaceship." He describes "needles in front of the luminous dials" and "red, yellow, green on the color indicator panel."

In *Vostok II* is what Titov calls the "world's most unique speedometer. Within a small black rectangle I could see the registering of white figures, not in miles or kilometers, but in the number of revolutions and decimal points of revolutions around the earth."

Titov operated his attitude-control system under manual status with "a polished black handle. The manual control fitted neatly into my clenched fist. There was a groove for each finger and a small white button beneath my thumb. . . ."

The Russians greatly extended their tracking and communications network for the flight of *Vostok II*. Throughout the USSR new ground tracking stations went up. In the Pacific and Atlantic were long rows of tracking ships, with emergency recovery areas clearly specified. Planes and helicopters were kept on constant alert status throughout the 17-orbit mission.

All communications from the global stations, as well as those from the spaceship, were automatically tape-recorded, and available for immediate playback at any time to meet any emergency situation. The USSR Ministry of Communications placed its powerful short-wave radio facilities on standby alert status to contact *Vostok II* no matter what its position around the world—a necessary move in view of the land mass of the earth covered, which came to almost the entire planet.

A Soviet communications engineer closely involved with the *Vostok II* mission describes the system:

"The computer center was working at full speed. Its electronic computers were specifying the parameters of the orbit, determining the descent area and performing calculations for the guidance to all stations keeping *Vostok II* under observation.

"As position data were received from the tracking stations they were immediately fed into electronic computers with the aid of special automatic devices. The computers worked out the commands to be transmitted aboard the spacecraft. In addition to this computer center [comparable to the Goddard Space Flight Center in Maryland], there were several other large centers located in different places to duplicate the most important calculations for greater reliability and accuracy.

"Small-size TV sets were installed in *Vostok II*. One of the TV receivers was situated right at the co-ordinating computer center. This made it possible to conduct TV observations directly from the center.

"The same center received part of the telemetric information direct from aboard the ship. The data obtained were immediately processed and transferred to the specialists.

"In order to deal with all systems installed in the spaceship the various specialists were working in different rooms of the co-ordinating computer center. By scanning the telemetric data transmitted to earth and comparing them with the cosmonaut's communications they were able to ascertain the workings of the spacecraft's instruments.

"A radiation-control team was working in one of the rooms of the co-ordinating computer center.

"Above-normal solar activity had been observed in the weeks preceding the launching. This might have led to more intense cosmic radiation, which had to be taken into account. Soviet stations and services keeping watch over solar activity and direct cosmic radiation intensity transmitted their observation data, measurements and predictions, to the center. A team of physicians and physicists was to establish whether the possible increase of cosmic radiation intensity could be dangerous. The data and inferences were reported by the radiation-control team to the cosmodrome authorities.

"Should danger arise during the flight, the decision to lower the spacecraft's orbiting altitude or even lower it would have to be taken."

Especially critical to the flight of *Vostok II* was the co-ordination during launch of communications and computing. After *Vostok II* was injected successfully into orbit . . .

"The first important moment had arrived. What were the period of rotation, apogee and perigee of the orbit? Did they differ from the calculated figures? Would it be necessary to rectify the flight program? Work proceeded at all computer centers at top speed and under utmost tension. In the meantime the cosmonaut relayed his reports: 'Everything is going fine. Everything on board the ship is in order. I feel very well. Tell me the orbit parameters.'

"Control data from stations began to arrive at the command post of the cosmodrome and at the co-ordinating computer center.

"The initial processing of orbital information ended. The exact orbital parameters were obtained. It was established that the deviations from the calculated figures were slight. This was very important. The information had to be passed on to the cosmonaut at once. He had to check the time with the earth and alter his navigating system in accordance with the more exact data. He had to know his true position precisely. It was not precluded that, depending on the way the cosmonaut felt, a landing would have to be made at a time unforeseen by the program.

"Time-checks and correction of navigational instruments were to be carried out throughout the whole flight, but the first checks were of particular importance.

"The second orbit began. According to the information from the computing center, the following information was relayed in succession to several radio stations: 'Orbit, normal; period of rotation, 88-6; apogee, 159.34 miles; perigee, 110.36 miles. Here are the corrections.'

"The cosmonaut knew exactly now where he was and started

Television monitor photograph of Titov in cabin of Vostok II

working in conformity with the flight assignment. He checked the spacecraft's manual controls, conducted observations, recorded information in the ship's log and simultaneously on the ship's compact tape recorder.

"Everything finally fell into proper routine at the beginning of the third orbit. . . ."

Notes on the Flight of Gherman Titov

As his booster rocket assembly thundered away from Baikonur, Titov pressed a button on his couch armrest and "an electric motor smoothly slid back the covering shield from a viewport near my head. Before my eyes the horizon expanded rapidly and the nearer surface of the earth was shrinking magically."

Within one hour of his launch, Titov was making his first tests of the *Vostok's* manual-control system. He reported that "it was easy and convenient to control the ship . . . it was possible to put it into any predetermined position at any time and to orient it to the necessary direction." Titov flew the spacecraft manually during this first orbit and once more, during the seventh orbit, to conduct more extensive tests of the attitude-control system."

One of the lesser-known aspects of Titov's flight is that immediately after insertion into orbit and separation from his booster rocket, the cosmonaut suffered complete spatial disorientation—vertigo: "I felt suddenly as though I were turning a somersault and then flying with my legs up. . . . I could not determine where I was . . . completely confused, unable to define where was the earth or the stars. . . . I was floating upside down, attached to nothing . . . the instrument panel was bobbing around somewhere alongside me. . . ."

Fortunately the sensation lasted only briefly, Titov explained. He said that he moved his head sharply and that "all of a sudden things began to focus properly and everything again became clear."

Titov's impressions of the earth from space—carried out in far more leisurely fashion, during his 25-hour flight, than Gaga-

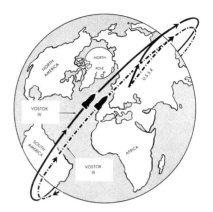

Orbital tracks of the Soviet spacecraft Vostok III *and* Vostok IV

rin's—are striking. He said that above all the "colors startled me . . . an extraordinary array of vivid hues that were strangely gentle in their play across the receding surface of the world."

He said that Africa is "distinctive in its markings; it is mainly a huge yellow mass wth green jungle sprinkled across the surface, almost like a strangely mottled leopard skin. I recognized the Sahara Desert as a vast ocean of golden-brown sands revealing not a single sign of life. . . ."

Some other descriptions: "The earth was remarkably beautiful from my altitude. . . . Blue coronas on the horizon were really indescribably beautiful. The stars seemed brighter than when seen from earth.

"I saw the moon twice. It was nearly a new moon and it looked just as it looks from earth. . . . The spaceship seemed to be standing still and the moon floating by.

". . . at one point in orbit the dazzling white peaks of the Himalayas and the Tien Shan Mountains lay squarely across my path of flight . . . they appeared as tiny white mounds separated by deep blue lines. . . .

". . . a shimmering light in the absolute blackness (during the third orbit) drew my attention. The light became ever more beautiful as I rushed closer and closer at nearly 18,000 miles per hour. . . . the lights came from the city of Rio de Janeiro. . . . The shimmering light became a wonderfully rich gold dust, sparkling and gleaming against a backdrop of velvet blackness. Then, as I passed almost over the city, I traced a network of

The four Russian cosmonauts during training. From the left are Andrian Nikolayev, who was later to pilot Vostok III; *Pavel Popovich, pilot of* Vostok IV; *Yuri Gagarin of* Vostok I, *and Gherman Titov of* Vostok II.

finely illuminated lines—the lighted highways of the city flowing in toward a central glow of orange. . . ."

The Soviet Space Twins

Staggering to the imagination as was the flight of Titov, it was a flight of minimal proportions compared to the sensational missions in August of 1962 of the third and fourth Russian cosmonauts. At 4:30 a.m. (EDT) on August 11, Major Andrian Grigoryvich Nikolayev was launched in *Vostok III* from Baikonur. Just less than 24 hours later, at 4:02 a.m. (EDT) on August 12, *Vostok IV*, carrying Lt. Colonel Pavel Romanovich Popovich thundered into an orbit that was almost a duplicate of that flown by Nikolayev.

The flights—which tested extensively the ability of the Russian countdown, support, launch, tracking, communications, and recovery systems—were astounding in both their complexity and their degree of competency. For the Russians revealed a competence far beyond our own by injecting the two spacecraft into orbits which brought them at their closest proximity to about 3.1 miles from each other, according to Popovich's statement at a joint press conference of the two cosmonauts in Moscow on August 21. Although they stated that there had been no attempt to effect an actual rendezvous, the implications of the Russian success are ominous. The extreme capabilities of the Russians are perhaps directly proportional to the strict orders of secrecy imposed upon American military officials who knew much more of the Soviet missions than they would say. But it was immediately apparent that the Russians had realized in mid-1962 a goal which the United States did not even plan to attempt! Nowhere in our Mercury, Dyna-Soar, Gemini, or Apollo programs —to be discussed at length in succeeding chapters—do we contemplate the simultaneous orbiting of two manned vehicles.

The Russians imposed greater secrecy on the flights of Nikolayev and Popovich than they had on previous missions. At the press conference Popovich gave the weight of the spacecraft at "about five tons," but few other details were released.

Both flights were launched with an orbital inclination of 64.59 degrees, the same as that for *Vostoks I* and *II*. The *corrected* orbital figures show that after one full orbit, *Vostok III* had a perigee of 111.85 miles and an apogee of 147.81 miles. Velocity was approximately 17,750 mph, and the orbital period 88.32 minutes.

Vostok IV had an initial perigee of 111.85 miles (exactly the same as *Vostok III*) and an initial apogee of 160.24 miles. The orbital period initially was 88.5 minutes.

Twelve hours after *Vostok IV* went into orbit, the spaceships were close to one another. *Vostok III*'s period was 88.2 minutes, and *Vostok IV*'s was 88.3 minutes. The apogees had become identical—141.41 miles. *Vostok III* had a perigee of 109.8 miles; *Vostok IV* was at a perigee of 110.5 miles.

Nikolayev remained in space for 64 orbits—a total of 94 hours and 25 minutes! Popovich accumulated a total of 48 orbits in

71 hours. The distance traveled is staggering—1,615,600 miles for Nikolayev, and 1,243,000 miles for Popovich.

Nikolayev landed first at a new recovery area some 373 miles east of Baikonur, near the town of Karaganda. Six minutes later, Popovich was on Russian soil. The landing places of the two men were about 124 miles apart. Both men were ejected from their spacecraft and came down by personal parachute.

Titov during his flight had eaten three complete meals—soup puree, meat and liver paste, and fruit juice. These were kept in large tubes; Titov unscrewed the end, placed the tube in his mouth, and squeezed. He once had the experience of spilling some juice and then watching the juice droplets floating before him. "They floated like berries before my face. They remained suspended in the air scarcely quivering. Finally, I caught them in the top of the tube and swallowed them."

Nikolayev and Popovich also had the same food tubes, but added small pieces of veal cutlets, chicken pies, sandwiches, fruit, coffee, water and fruit juice.

The third and fourth cosmonauts carried out extensive experiments, many of them similar to those of Titov. The single greatest departure was in their releasing their harnesses and during each orbit when they were awake, drifting and floating about their cabins. This one feat more than any other provided bright encouragement for space doctors in both the USSR and the United States.

The single most vital aspect of Titov's flight was the sensations of mild nausea and dizziness he suffered during his ninth hour in space. While these did not interfere with his work, they were greatly aggravating. Titov's discomfort threatened serious difficulties in sustained space flights of the future, and after the cosmonaut's mission, the Russians accelerated their program of biomedical research, notably in respect to prolonged weightlessness. Emphasis was placed upon increasing the stability of the balance-sensing system of the inner ear in an attempt to overcome the sensations experienced by Titov. The training program involved the use of simulator devices such as "looping-revolving swings, batounde or circus spring board, rhoenrad" and other equipment. The cosmonauts practiced severe calisthenics and acrobatics, then doing a headstand for 30 seconds, resuming the acrobatics, returning to the headstand, etc. Whatever the final program details, there is no question but that they worked.

Speaking of floating freely in space, Nikolayev said. "It is very interesting to experience this condition when one is not strapped to the chair. During every orbit in conformity with the program I unstrapped myself and got out of the chair.

"In free soaring a person simply hangs in space touching neither the walls nor the floor. If one does a turn then he begins to turn around his axis like a whirligig.

"When it is necessary to move, one simply pushes lightly against the wall and he floats lightly and evenly. The movements of the arms and legs retain their coordination. . . . I carried out communications and ate. In a condition of weightlessness one can live and work completely."

The new series of Cosmos satellites that started off the year for the Soviets (eight satellites orbited from March 16 to August 18, besides the *Vostoks III* and *IV*) were of approximately 10,000 pounds payload, and were instrumented to provide data along a wide spectrum of space conditions, including information especially applicable to manned spaceships.

Forecast for late 1962 and 1963: Additional manned orbital flights, especially with two or more men in a single spaceship. Missions that will accomplish rendezvous, and the docking of the spaceships. The cosmonauts will leave their spaceships and float freely in space (attached by safety lines). The cosmonauts will transfer from one spacecraft to another. They will change the orbits of their spaceships while in flight.

Simultaneously, a massive lunar-study and exploration program will get under way.

Barring any unexpected disasters, the first manned flights around the moon and back will be a reality before the end of 1963.

A Russian reality, that is.

IX : *The Suborbital Flights of Shepard and Grissom*

THE STRANGEST ASPECT of the suborbital space flights in May and July of 1961 of Astronauts Alan B. Shepard, Jr., and Virgil I. Grissom are that these two suborbital flights are the first, and quite likely to be the last *intended* suborbital space missions ever flown. Only a few years past, the concept of even the high, looping ballistic flight trajectory of a sealed life-supporting capsule that contained a man created great excitement among space scientists. Such a mission was regarded as indispensable to the furtherance of the science of manned flight in space. Engineers designed a host of special vehicles, and dozens of elaborately prepared plans for suborbital flight weighed down the tables of government authorities.

None of these flourished. And not until Project Mercury was conceived in late 1958 as a cautious, step-by-step learning process toward manned space flight did the suborbital manned mission suddenly acquire the project stature for which engineers had so long hoped.

In the laborious process of learning—as much about the reactions of the man in space as about the reliability of the spacecraft—we came to look upon the suborbital flight as an indispensable step. It permitted immediate availability of a rocket booster—the "Old Reliable" Redstone missile. Compared to the more elaborate and later creations of the missile era, the Redstone is the ultimate in simplicity—and in reliability as well.

It had power sufficient to achieve speeds unprecedented in our manned-flight science—5,000 miles per hour. It could loft the Mercury capsule high out of the atmosphere into space. It could subject its occupant to high acceleration forces, even higher deceleration forces, to the space environment, and to the unknown factor of weightlessness. Even more important, it retained the astronaut in that space environment for the briefest of periods—approximately five minutes. Since capsule re-entry and recovery were wholly automatic, even if the man were incapacitated, he would be returned quickly enough to the earth —no more than 300 miles and some 15 minutes from his point of departure.

And while these processes were diligently pursued, other engineers could complete the long process of preparing the only rocket in the country capable of orbital flight with the Mercury spacecraft—the Atlas.

Using the Redstone booster, the capsule would be subjected to acceleration, friction, high dynamic air forces acting upon its surfaces, possible activation of its escape system, and a complete run-through of its automatic systems; it would separate from its booster while in a weightless condition, execute its automatic turnaround, test its stabilization system under zero gravity, follow an autopilot-controlled maneuver series under zero gravity; it would supply a complete life-environment system to its occupant and permit that occupant to exercise—however briefly —manual override of the automatic systems; the capsule would re-enter the atmosphere, endure deceleration, and survive friction with the atmosphere. Once back in the atmosphere, it would follow a sequence of automatic events in recovery— drogue chute, main chute operation, activation of recovery aids, and recovery.

The tests of this nature would permit a progressive improvement in capsule design and modification of future capsules.

With all these things in mind, the planners of Project Mercury scheduled three suborbital flights in 1961 as a basic minimum in the man in space development program.

Something cut the number down to two flights. That "something" is not a definite item to set aside, but a combination of events and conclusions.

It began with the orbital flight of Yuri Gagarin. While we still waited for the brief, hesitant suborbital flight, the Russians plunged fully into manned space flight. Then came two Redstone-boosted missions, both extremely successful. And *then* came that brilliant space journey of 17 orbits of Gherman Titov—while our space time for both missions amounted barely to ten minutes above the atmosphere.

With both suborbital flights successful, and a national pride wincing under the spectacular missions of Gagarin and Titov, the third suborbital flight never left the ground. And the man who had been the backup to Shepard and Grissom—John H. Glenn—moved into the number one position to be the first American, and the third man, to orbit the planet earth.

The Flight of Freedom 7

To the eyes and ears of most Americans, the first manned space mission began with a dress rehearsal for the flight long in the future—the orbital rush about the globe. The curtain to the drama of Alan Shepard's brief flight into space rose on the morning of April 25, 1961—11 days before Shepard left the concrete surface of Pad 5 on Cape Canaveral. It was the opening curtain because a great army of press, with elaborate television and radio coverage, had thronged to Cape Canaveral to report the event. Almost as a tasty prelude to Shepard's flight, in which interest was overwhelming, NASA planned to fire into orbit an unmanned Mercury capsule. The proximity of the dates is incidental, but nevertheless it did provide a spectacular introduction to Americans of what a space mission could become.

On a clear and beautiful April 25th morning, the countdown moved through several technical holds to its fateful moment of zero. We looked across Cape Canaveral at a scene we knew we would come back at some undetermined time—we hoped in the same year—to see once more: the towering Atlas booster, sides frosted with ice, gleaming in the morning sun; and atop that powerful rocket, the Mercury capsule. This was the first attempt to orbit that spacecraft—something the Russians had already done five times with unmanned 10,000-pound spaceships, and then once more, but the sixth time with a man.

The April 25th shot—Mercury-Atlas 3—was terribly important. Atlas came alive with her familiar two lances of vernier flame; mountains of steam boiled into the sky, lashed by the violence of the flame bucket. Atlas lifted as her yellow steel clamps sprang back, clearing the heavy machine for a flight of golden-booster fire. The roar rumbled toward us and then broke in a wave of overwhelming sound, a beautiful cry of energy that seemed to shake the very ground of the Cape.

She lifted up, higher and higher, standing out brilliantly and clearly against the deep blue sky. But none of us watching the sight knew at the moment that the autopilot had failed to respond to its duty; this dereliction in turn resulted in an Atlas that rose in a perfect, flawless demonstration of power—but *straight up*. The rocket failed to roll and turn; her progress became a potential peril, and in Central Control a switch was closed.

Three miles high, where there had been a mighty creature embarked on its journey into space, there appeared first a tiny lick of flame, a scarlet lance. The lance speared deeply, and then the heavens in front of us tore asunder as a smear of deep, blood-red flame and seething smoke replaced that clean, shining rocket. A great angry red eye swirled into existence, and then shredded into a greasy blotch as the smoke spread and chunks of flaming Atlas tumbled helplessly from the sky.

A failure? Certainly; the black box, so important to the mission, had failed to operate. A rocket had been flawless in its operation, but no matter.

What did matter was the escape system of the Mercury spacecraft as it was linked electronically to Atlas. The escape rocket blazed with energy; it flung back fire and smoke, and ripped the capsule free from the Atlas. The capsule soared up and to the side; it began to fall, and it came back to earth as automatic systems clicked and whirred. The capsule returned to the surface of the ocean in gentle fashion, swaying beneath its parachute. Its damage was negligible, if it could even be considered damaged. It was good to know—some months later—that this same capsule, labeled MA-4, did race around the world in a single, "perfect" orbital flight.

But back in the spring of 1961 . . . 11 days after the explosive charges gutted the Atlas, Alan Shepard was ready to go. We had been through the unhappy but not unexpected problems of weather—fierce squalls, sheets of rain, and vivid lightning bolts—and, of course, delays and postponements. But on this morning, May 5, things were in readiness.

In the predawn darkness the Redstone stood as a brilliant shaft on her pad, emblazoned in the searchlights of gleaming white. By four in the morning Shepard started on his way; like Glenn, whose mission was yet to come, Shepard then waited in the transfer van near the rocket. At 5:15 a.m. he rode the elevator to the level called Surfside 5—where he would enter the capsule.

The two rockets—Redstone and Atlas—were different to a startling degree. Redstone weighed 33 tons—nearly 100 tons *less* than Atlas. The differences were essentially the gross disproportion in power: 78,000 pounds thrust for Redstone, and 362,000 pounds thrust for Atlas. But their goals were not the same.

At 18 minutes past five a.m. Shepard was comfortably placed on his contour couch in *Freedom 7*, his spacecraft. At 6:10 a.m. technicians sealed the hatch.

The countdown went through its normally infuriating delays —an inverter that needed replacement, squalls and other elements of poor weather. At 9:17 a.m. a long countdown delay was eliminated and the count resumed at T minus 14:30. We went down to a finger-gnawing T minus 2:40 when a cry of "*Hold!*" came, so engineers could check a pressure gauge.

Thirteen seconds after 9:34 a.m., the Redstone splashed golden fire on the concrete of Pad 5; the flame whipped sideways across a needle-pointed metal flame deflector and lashed the concrete.

Much, much more so than we would know with Glenn or

Alan Shepard lifts on May 5, 1961, atop Redstone rocket booster from Cape Canaveral, Florida, for our first suborbital flight.

Carpenter, the Cape rang with the cries of emotion, the anguish, the hoarse shouting to *"Go! Go! Go, Baby, Go!"* Redstone lifted from the earth with not a flaw. Perfectly she rose, booming deep in thunder that came back to us, startlingly loud. She rejected the earth, embraced acceleration and speed, and ran away from the planet. Her flame was clean and sharp, a line of shock diamonds bristling in the clear morning air. Straight up, then her flame lashing furiously, a golden ball at her tail.

From the capsule Shepard called: "Roger . . . liftoff . . . the clock is started." Deke Slayton at capsule communications in Mercury Control: "Okay, you're on your way."

The Redstone scrambled away from earth and knifed upward into vacuum. She shouldered her way past some clouds and then shrank to a dot before disappearing from sight.

The engine shut down with a Redstone velocity of 5,280 miles per hour—Alan Shepard was on his way for a flight to 115 miles above the earth and 302 miles downgrade from Canaveral. From start to finish the journey would last 15 minutes 22 seconds.

On the morning of May 5 I wrote there on the Cape the aspects of the flight in regard to the astronaut:

> The performance this morning of Alan Shepard was astounding in its crispness and matter-of-fact control of everything that was happening. The mission seemed more like a practice run than an actual flight into space with all the real and grim dangers that it presented to that lone human being inside his capsule. Shepard's performance can be described only as flawless, or as close to perfection as one could ever possibly expect. It was astonishing to hear. It lent more of a sense of unreality than anything else to the mission. We heard the voice of a skilled test pilot, in absolute command of himself and his situation, utterly confident, believing in his team and in his equipment.
>
> It was the most incredible human performance I have ever had the great privilege to hear.
>
> Alan Shepard followed every single phase of the flight with an efficiency that became ever more astounding. His ability to control his spacecraft, to work his instruments, to call out readings by radio even when he was subjected to the fierce pressures of plus-gravity and crushing deceleration forces, left listeners flabbergasted. He reported on his control-system fuel supply, the amount of g-forces he was experiencing, his cabin pressure

The earth as seen by Shepard from 115 miles above the Atlantic

in pounds per square inch, everything called for in a tight-fitting and exhausting program.

At 9:38:30 a.m. came those wonderful words from the first American in space: *"What a beautiful view!"* *Freedom 7* was 115 miles above the earth, and Shepard scanned a view of 1,600 miles at the moment. Because the re-entry into the atmosphere came at a steeper angle than would be achieved with orbital flight, Shepard endured in his descent a force of 11g, a 3g greater force than that to be experienced by Glenn in his three-orbit mission.

On Canaveral we listened by short-wave radio to the reports of what was happening as the capsule lowered beneath its parachute. We could hear the thundering cheers of the men on the deck of the aircraft carrier USS *Lake Champlain* as helicopter No. 44 brought America's first spaceman aboard.

It had been a wonderful flight, everything we hoped it could

Marine helicopter of carrier recovery force hooks capsule, then hovers carefully while cable winch pulls up Shepard.

turn out to be. It signaled the start of suborbital flight number two—this time with Virgil I. Grissom.

The Flight of Liberty Bell 7

On July 21, 1961—after the familiar routine of holds, delays, and a two-day scrub—Virgil I. Grissom rose in his Mercury spacecraft *Liberty Bell 7* from Cape Canaveral at 7:20 a.m. His speed was slightly higher than that of Shepard—5,310 miles per hour —and Grissom rose in his ballistic arc to 118 miles altitude and 305 miles downrange from the Cape.

Liberty Bell 7 incorporated important modifications from the *Freedom 7* capsule flown by Shepard (Shepard's capsule was No. 7; Grissom's No. 11) some two months previously. Readily obvious as a modification was the large window in Grissom's capsule that replaced the ten-inch porthole which Shepard used for observations. Changes also were made in instrumental panel and instrument layout. The Grissom capsule used the explosively actuated hatch for the first time in the Mercury flight, and minor changes were made in the capsule-control system. To overcome a 15-second period of intense vibration during Shepard's ascent, engineers modified for the Grissom flight the junction between the rocket and the capsule to eliminate the vibrations.

Two days before he lifted from Canaveral, it seemed that Grissom might have been on his way. On the morning of July 19 Grissom had been in the capsule for several hours. Hopes were high that morning that "Gus" would be able to become rocket-borne. But thick clouds swept low over the Cape, scudding rapidly before a strong wind—much the same as on the morning of February 20, 1962, when Glenn blasted off into orbit. The difference, however, was that on the morning of July 19 the clouds kept increasing in number and thickness. A towering thunderhead loomed blackly off the edge of the Cape, and in the distance, marching closer to the launch area, were several white-gray squall lines.

Two days later, on the 21st, the weather still was poor. But a break had been forecast for a period of about one hour, and during that time—with a "great big hole full of blue sky" over Canaveral—Grissom was on his way.

During the flight, Grissom's rocket burned for eight-tenths second longer than did the booster for Shepard. That was enough to change the performance slightly. Grissom's flight was 30 miles per hour faster, 1.5 miles higher, and three miles longer in distance. Shepard was weightless for four minutes 41 seconds; Grissom, for five minutes 18 seconds.

Virgil Grissom performed in a fashion that the Mercury officials called "superb." During his flight he used to good advantage his larger viewing window ($19 \times 11 \times 7.5$ inches) to study the sights briefly available to him. At 36,000 feet, moving upward at just above the speed of sound and accelerating rapidly, the capsule whipped through a thin layer of clouds and then out into the sun. The sky, Grissom said, became deep blue and then with an unexpected suddenness it was black. He reported that he saw only one star (it turned out to be Venus) and that the views of space "fascinated" him.

Some of his comments during his debriefing:

"The Cape is the best [visual] reference I had. . . . I could pick out the Banana River and see the peninsula that runs on down south, and then on down the coast of Florida. I saw what must have been West Palm Beach . . . and it was a dark brown color and quite large. I never did see Cuba. High cirrus blotted out everything except an area from about Daytona Beach back inland to Orlando and Lakeland to Lake Okeechobee and down to the tip of Florida. Beyond this the Gulf of Mexico was visible."

Grissom described the horizon as "very smooth as far as I could see . . . a blue band above the earth, then the dark sky. It is very vivid when you go from the blue to the dark. . . . The blue band appears about a quarter of an inch wide."

Unlike Shepard, Grissom had some problems with sunlight: "The sun was coming in bright at $0.05g$ [beginning of re-entry] and . . . it comes in pretty much as a shaft of light with everything else in the cockpit dark."

(Above) *A jubilant Shepard is greeted on Grand Bahama Island by Deke Slayton (left) and Virgil Grissom (far right).* (Below) *Less than three months later, Grissom took the final walk to the Redstone booster that sent him into space at more than 5,000 mph.*

Looking through the periscope after jettisoning the retropack: "Right after retro-jettison, I saw something floating around. It actually looked like a retromotor at one time, and these floated by a couple of times."

During re-entry Grissom reported seeing shock waves (these have been observed in rocket-powered supersonic aircraft flights): "I'm fairly certain it was shock waves off the shield of the capsule. It looked like smoke or contrail really, but I'm pretty certain it was shocks."

Grissom's reaction to zero gravity was more of a visual cue than a bodily sensation: ". . . At zero g, everything is floating around. I could see washers and trash floating around. I had no other feeling of zero g; in fact, I felt just about like I did at $1g$ on my back or sitting up."

Grissom experienced a mild disorientation—a slight pitching forward at cutoff of the booster: "Right at BECO when the tower went, I got a little tumbling sensation. I can't recall which way it was that I felt I tumbled, but I did get the same sort of feeling that we had on the centrifuge. There was a definite second of disorientation there. I knew what it was, so it didn't bother me."

In retrofire: "Prior to retrofire, I really felt that I was moving; I was going backwards. . . . When the retros fired, I had the impression I was very definitely going the other way."

Other comments by Astronaut Grissom on his MR-4 (Mercury-Redstone 4) flight, of special interest:

". . . I felt the launch vehicle start to vibrate [at the moment of ignition] and could hear the engine start. . . . The powered flight portion of the mission was in general very smooth. A low-order vibration started at approximately T plus 50 seconds, but it did not develop above a low level and was undetectable after about T plus 70 seconds. . . . The magnitude of the acceleration corresponds well to the launch simulations on the centrifuge, but the onset was much smoother.

" . . . Launch-vehicle engine cutoff was sudden and I could not sense any tail-off of the launch vehicle. I did feel . . . a very brief tumbling sensation. The firing of the escape-tower clamp ring and escape rocket is quite audible and I could see the escape rocket motor and tower throughout its tail-off burning phase and for what seemed like quite some time after that climbing off to my right.

". . . The posigrade firing is a very audible bang and a definite kick, producing a deceleration of approximately 1g. Prior to this time, the spacecraft was quite stable with no apparent motion. As the posigrade rockets separated the spacecraft from the launch vehicle, the spacecraft angular motions and angular accelerations were quite apparent.

". . . The spacecraft turnaround to retrofire attitude is quite a weird maneuver to ride through. At first, I thought the spacecraft might be tumbling and out of control. A quick check of the instruments indicated that turnaround was proceeding much as those experienced on the procedures trainer, with the exception of roll attitude which appeared to be very slow and behind the schedule that I was expecting.

". . . During re-entry . . . and until main parachute employment, there is a noticeable roar and a mild buffeting of the spacecraft. This is probably the noise of a blunt object moving rapidly through the atmosphere and the buffeting is not distracting nor does it interfere with pilot function."

The Loss of the Capsule

The modification to Grissom's capsule of the explosively activated hatch almost cost the astronaut his life. Engineers and the astronauts agreed after the Shepard flight that the capsule must be capable of immediate jettisoning in an emergency on or under the water. A small explosive cord was wound around the hatch; the cord was percussion-activated. As Grissom landed:

"The spacecraft landing in the water was a mild jolt; not hard enough to cause discomfort or disorientation. The spacecraft recovery section went under the water and I had the feeling that I was on my left side and slightly head down. The window was completely covered with water and there was a disconcerting gurgling noise. A quick check showed no water entering the spacecraft. The spacecraft started to slowly right itself; as soon as I was sure the recovery section was out of the water, I ejected the reserve parachute by actuating the recovery aids switch. The spacecraft then righted itself rapidly.

"I felt that I was in good condition at this point and started to prepare myself for egress. I had previously opened the faceplate and had disconnected the visor seal while descending on the main parachute. The next moves in order were to disconnect the oxygen outlet hose at the helmet, unfasten the helmet from the suit, release the chest strap, release the lap belt and shoulder harness, release the knee straps, disconnect the biomedical sensors, and roll up the neck dam. The neck dam is a rubber diaphragm that is fastened on the exterior of the suit, below the helmet attaching ring. After the helmet is disconnected, the neck dam is rolled around the ring and up around the neck, similar to a turtle-neck sweater. This left me connected to the spacecraft at two points, the oxygen inlet hose which I needed for cooling and the helmet communications lead.

"At this time I turned my head to the door. First, I released the restraining wires at both ends and tossed them toward my feet. Then I removed the knife from the door and placed it in the survival pack. The next task was to remove the cover and safety pin from the hatch detonator. I felt at this time that everything had gone nearly perfect and that I would go ahead and mark the switch position chart as had been requested.

"After about three or four minutes, I instructed the helicopter to come on in and hook onto the spacecraft and confirmed the egress procedures with him. I unhooked my oxygen inlet hose and was lying on the couch, waiting for the helicopter's call to blow the hatch. I was lying flat on my back at this time and I had turned my attention to the knife in the survival pack, wondering if there might be some way I could carry it out with me as a souvenir. I heard the hatch blow [at his press conference, Grissom said that all of a sudden came a "POW!"—and the hatch was gone]—the noise was a dull thud—and looked up to see the

Astronaut Grissom came perilously close to death during his flight of July 25, 1961. When the capsule hatch blew open, and the sea poured in, Grissom went out—fast. In a desperate attempt to save the spacecraft, Marine helicopter (above) drops its wheels into the ocean. Finally saved from the sea—where he was sinking because of water pouring into his spacesuit—Grissom was grateful to reach carrier (below) where doctors helped remove his water-logged spacesuit.

blue sky out the hatch and water start to spill in over the door-sill. Just a few minutes before, I had gone over egress procedures in my mind and I reacted instinctively. I lifted the helmet from my head and dropped it, reached for the right side of the instrument panel, and pulled myself through the hatch.

"After I was in the water and away from the spacecraft, I noticed a line from the dye-marker can over my shoulder. The spacecraft was obviously sinking and I was concerned that I might be pulled down with it. I freed myself from the line and noticed that I was floating with my shoulders above water.

"The helicopter was on top of the spacecraft at this time with all three of its landing gear in the water. I thought the copilot was having difficulty hooking onto the spacecraft and I swam the four or five feet to give him some help. Actually, he had cut the antennae and hooked the spacecraft in record time.

"The helicopter pulled up and away from me with the spacecraft and I saw the personnel sling start down; then the sling was pulled back into the helicopter and it started to move away from me. At this time, I knew that a second helicopter had been assigned to pick me up, so I started to swim away from the primary helicopter. I apparently got caught in the rotorwash between the two helicopters because I could not get close to the second helicopter, even though I could see the copilot in the door with a horsecollar swinging in the water. I finally reached the horsecollar and by this time, I was getting quite exhausted. When I first got into the water, I was floating quite high up; I would say my armpits were just about at the water level. But the neck dam was not up tight and I had forgotten to lock the oxygen inlet port; so the air was gradually seeping out of my suit. Probably the most air was going out around the neck dam, but I could see that I was gradually sinking lower and lower in the water and was having a difficult time staying afloat. Before the copilot finally got the horsecollar to me, I was going under water quite often. The mild swells we were having were breaking over my head and I was swallowing some salt water. As I reached the horsecollar, I slipped into it and I knew that I had it on backwards; but I gave the 'up' signal and held on because I knew that I wasn't likely to slip out of the sling. As soon as I got into the helicopter, my first thought was to get on a life preserver so that if anything happened to the helicopter, I wouldn't have another ordeal in the water. . . ."

As the astronaut was picked up, the other helicopter tried vainly to retrieve *Liberty Bell 7* from the ocean. But within moments the space capsule was swamped. The empty spacecraft weighed some 2,100 pounds. The landing bag beneath the spacecraft filled with 8,000 pounds of sea water. Several thousand pounds' additional weight in the form of water poured in through the hatch. The combined weight apparently proved to be beyond the lifting capacity of the single-engine Sikorsky HUS helicopter.

Despite valiant efforts on the part of the crew, they had no choice but to cut the cable free (the capsule sank in 16,000 feet of water) when an engine-overheat warning light flashed on. It seemed certain that the engine was overheating and might burn; certainly it would lose power. If this happened the capsule would drag the helicopter down to crash into the sea. The crew cut the spacecraft loose and rushed to the aircraft carrier for an emergency landing.

There was an ironic twist to this episode. On the carrier a careful check of the helicopter engine and control system revealed that the engine had never really overheated—and that the fire-warning signal was due in fact to a faulty wiring circuit!

But the astronaut was safe, he had performed as hoped, and the mission in this respect was a complete success.

By now we had learned enough. The suborbital program had produced all that we could determine toward preparing for orbital flight.

John Glenn began to prepare for his mission in space.

X: *Transition from Mercury*

"WE HAVE PIPED man aboard as the pilot of spacecraft. Now we can get rid of some of that automatic equipment and let man take over."

In this fashion Astronaut John Glenn summarized his three-orbit mission in space. As the months and years pass, Mercury-Atlas 6 will come to be regarded as the turning point in the American man-in-space program. In the long run, perhaps, the failure of the stabilization equipment aboard *Friendship 7*—the second consecutive failure of this type with the capsule in orbit —may be one of the most fortuitous events in these early days of the exploration of space.

Until Glenn returned to earth, the astronaut's place in Project Mercury was actually a secondary role. Difficult as this may be to understand from the viewpoint of the man in the street, it gains reality when we consider that from the very outset the Mercury capsule had been designed as a completely automatic system. It did not matter whether or not the man was aboard the spacecraft. His role could be ignored by the spacecraft systems, and he would be retained as a passive passenger rather than as an integral element of the spacecraft.

"A passenger in an automated vehicle . . ." This is how one Mercury engineer described the spacecraft system and its astronaut *prior* to the Glenn flight. But afterward? More than an integral, active operating element of the spacecraft system—the man now becomes the *primary* source of control, of decision making,

of direction of the mission, and as the *only* means truly of meeting the "unexpected situation."

Beyond question the meaning of Glenn's performance aboard
Friendship 7 carries with it deep currents of re-evaluating both
philosophically and technically the role of man in space. It is
astonishing how many scientists in this country have been opposed from the outset of the $400,000,000 Mercury program to
the entire project. Man in space, they felt, was a stunt—a worthless patchwork of technological gadgetry without true value or
scientific reward. As such, it was a flagrant abuse of the nation's
scientific talent and an unforgivable drain upon its financial and
technological resources.

It was stupid, asserted this large body of scientists, to send
man into space with his limited capabilities in terms of his
senses, when instruments could do as well or actually much
better than man in space, could remain there for greater periods
of time, could be subjected to much greater stresses and forces
(such as radiation), and could observe, record, and report on
thousands of items which lie totally beyond the senses of man to
discover and to observe.

In some respects, this attitude is entirely correct. In others, its
value is questionable. But in many other respects of flight beyond
the earth it is totally wrong.

As the missions of Glenn and Carpenter not only proved—but
reiterated—the reliability of automatic equipment is still more of
a quest than it is a reality. The dependence upon instruments for
accuracy still is riddled with too many question marks. The
machine is no panacea for the problems of space flight and undoubtedly it never will be in its robot form.

The flight of Astronaut Malcolm Scott Carpenter on May 24,
1962, in the capsule *Aurora 7*, despite opinions to the contrary,
did not alter this philosophy. There are some who insist that
Carpenter's flight was a partial failure.

Although there is always room for human error and human
failure, and we shall undoubtedly face this problem as we continue in our probing of space, "failure" is entirely out of context
in regard to Mercury-Atlas 7.

Navy's Sikorsky HSS amphibious helicopter practices retrieval of Mercury capsule from ocean.

Carpenter was unable to complete all the tasks assigned to him, and he faced danger because of an intensive drive—impossible to fulfill—to complete all the many tasks which he was attempting to meet. He was overloaded. A machine would have broken down completely—the man did not.

We are still probing to determine the capacities and limitations of man in space. Carpenter's flight, just as was Glenn's—and as many more flights to come will be—was essentially a mission of experimentation and research. The hard truth of the matter is that many of the so-called "failures" experienced by Carpenter have turned out to be erroneous readings of instruments from the ground! Again it has been a case not of the man proving inadequate, but of the inability of instruments to record, transmit, and display accurately to men on the ground exactly what was happening out in space.

Carpenter proved what we learned with excitement from Glenn's flight—that visual acuity of the human "seeing system" is far more capable than we had suspected. Not only did Carpenter determine that international orange in a dayglo (brilliant

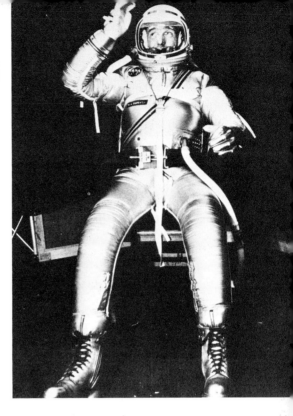

Astronaut Malcolm Scott Carpenter . . . America's second man to orbit the earth.

reflection material) color, as well as highly reflective silver, could be seen with the greatest accuracy and depth perception in space, but he was able also to track the Atlas booster as it trailed him, to observe that the mylar plastic balloon tethered behind his capsule did not inflate completely, and that it both stretched taut behind the capsule and sometimes wandered about in coils and loops within the range of the long line attaching it to the capsule. That all these scenes and activities were entirely clear to Carpenter is cheering news to all those concerned with the development of the rendezvous and docking techniques which we plan to use in orbit and ultimately to employ for landings on the moon before this decade is over.

Consistently during Carpenter's flight minor equipment items failed or malfunctioned. And consistently throughout the flight the ability of the man to modify and to control this equipment was demonstrated. The flight—although this may seem somewhat strange to those who read headlines of possible disaster—actually proved to be the best single vindication of the integrity of the Mercury capsule.

We saw demonstrated the same relationship between astronaut and capsule that exists between pilot and aircraft. Things do not always work as planned in aircraft . . . and the pilot is usually able to compensate for the deficiencies that occur.

Carpenter overshot his scheduled landing point by some 250 miles. Was this a "failure"? In respect to not landing precisely where planned, it was. But considering that this was the second orbital flight ever made by this country, the term "failure" is inappropriate. And the important thing, above all else, is the fact that the emergency beacon system worked well, the emergency search and rescue worked perfectly, and that Carpenter suffered no ill effects and was brought back to the United States in excellent condition.

By what other criteria is a flight to be judged?

Man, obviously, cannot venture into space without automatic, semi-automatic, and extensive equipment—no more than he can fly at 50,000 feet without extensive equipment and protection. But the philosophy underlying manned atmospheric flight—the integration of man and machine into a single man-machine system, with the man as the central core of authority and control and decision making—now appears to be applying with equal intensity to man in space.

The evaluation of Glenn's space mission not only struck hard at immediate flights that were planned, but also shook mightily the structure of the philosophy for the programs scheduled for future years. Our plans for two-man Gemini spaceships, for three-man Apollo spaceships for lunar flights—these and many other space programs have been designed from the outset with all the ponderous redundancy of totally automatic systems, in which the role of the human passengers remained relegated to passivity. The men would participate actively in the missions involved, but they would not be *necessary*—and if they made the flights essentially as so much vegetable matter, that, too, lay within the framework of command and function of the robot systems. The men would be transported to the moon so that they might observe and comment, but they were not essential, so to speak, to the spaceship reaching the moon and returning.

All this has vanished in that single hard evaluation of what happened to Glenn and Carpenter in space—and of the manner in which they responded and performed.

Alan Shepard has keynoted one vital area in future operations that has already undergone a design philosophy revolution. Prior to Mercury-Atlas 6, Shepard explained, the question of the visibility of the stars in daylight to the human eye was unresolved. Because this question had never been answered, navigation in space between the earth and the moon was considered primarily—or wholly—an automated affair linked constantly with vast computer facilities on the earth as well as those within the spacecraft itself. But because Glenn could observe clearly and sharply the stars in space during his flight over the "day side" of earth, this immediately makes it not only possible, but extremely probable, that an astronaut in space can determine his exact position by observing the stars and using his findings to establish his position—in quite precisely the same manner that ancient mariners and ocean-flying pilots have always done.

Shepard estimates that an astronaut in "deep space" in the vicinity of the earth and the moon could determine within an accuracy of ten miles his position in space—which lies well within general accuracy requirements for a flight from the earth to the moon. Finer readings in terms of position to different world surfaces, in respect to the earth and moon, would then be determined with the aid of instruments, just as the pilot of an airplane requires sensitive altimeters to determine his exact altitude above (1) the sea-level surface of the planet and (2) the altitude above the terrain immediately below his aircraft. The difference is that the man-machine system is being used, rather than the machine system with the man as the passive observer.

Robert R. Gilruth, Director of Project Mercury, has no doubts about the ability of his astronauts to perform celestial navigation in space. "We now figure that we can get a real accurate fix," he stated.

[The author would be ignoring an element of the man-machine philosophy at this point if he did not stress to the reader the fact that many months before Glenn's flight, a number of these same conclusions, if not all, were arrived at by the Russians after the flight of *Vostok II*. One of the primary tasks assigned to Gherman Titov was the observation of celestial bodies both during day and night exposure in his orbits, and his 25 hours in space permitted him a vastly greater range of observation than was possible in the four hours 40 minutes' time spent by Glenn in orbit. To ignore the Russian program in this instance, and leave the impression that these conclusions were drawn *only* after the Glenn flight, is to leave the reader with an incorrect picture of the situation. Glenn provided proof in the most dramatic form for the *American* space program that these conclusions were to be drawn; because of his emergency situation in orbit and his imperative *need* for manned control of his craft, he may, and likely did, provide even greater emphasis to these points than did the flight of Titov without the mechanical failures that attended the orbits of *Friendship 7*.]

Dr. William K. Douglas (lieutenant colonel, US Air Force and the astronauts' personal physician) summed up the feeling of the project personnel when he declared that Glenn's flight showed conclusively that man "is a heck of a lot better than a black box."

Walter C. Williams, the Mercury Operations Director, has, behind his work in Mercury, a vast store of experience with test pilots. Williams was one of the key personnel in the development of the X-series of rocket-powered aircraft that were the first ever to exceed the speed of sound, to fly at more than twice the speed of sound, to encounter compressibility and friction in flight at levels never known, to reach out to greater heights than man had ever attained. In this capacity, Walt Williams has the most practiced eye and the "feeling" for manned test missions.

He stated after Glenn's return that the astronaut's performance aboard his capsule in space was as good as that ever flown by any test pilot on an experimental mission—and that is saying a lot. Coming from Williams, it is a rousing vindication of the role that man will play in the future.

In his flight, Glenn made extensive body tests to determine his reaction to weightlessness. As he described in his official report, he turned his head from side to side, rolled his head, and shook it back and forth (in yaw, roll, and pitch). These experiments were a direct result of the difficulties that Titov experienced in orbit. Glenn had no problems of any kind with zero gravity and, indeed, enjoyed the sensation greatly—as did Gagarin and, until he experienced his dizziness and nausea, so did Titov.

During the time of the Glenn flight, more information was being brought into the United States, and delivered to the medical people in Project Mercury, of Titov's reactions in training and in space—reactions that have great bearing upon the sensations attributable to sustained weightlessness. That information is vital, but it was never obtainable by the Project Mercury personnel through "normal channels."

This illustrates the great need for closer co-operation among the various manned space programs carried out by the USSR and the United States. Incidentally, there is an aside to the Titov story that few Americans know—that none, apparently, knew at the time of the Russian flight.

The biographical data on Titov states clearly that he and his wife, Tamara, have no children. But no one knew that the Titovs had a son, Igor. As an infant, Igor grew deathly ill. The nature of his malady could not be determined by Soviet doctors—and they are among the finest in the world. Igor slowly lost the vitality of life and Titov, in the midst of his final preparations for flight into space, suffered the loss of his son. I discussed this matter with one of the key medical directors of our manned space program. He reflected on the death of the boy and then said: "It's too bad, really, that we can't work closer with these people in a program such as this . . . who knows, we might have known something in this country that could have saved that child's life."

But such co-operation does not yet exist. The author would not attempt even to hazard an opinion as to whether or not we will ever work with the Soviets on a more co-operative basis than now exists, but, from both viewpoints, manned space flight certainly would seem to benefit from the arrangement.

Changes in Design Philosophy

When Glenn completed his mission in *Friendship 7*, the National Aeronautics and Space Administration had available eight Mercury capsules and eight Atlas boosters to conclude the project. Four of the capsules were allocated to additional three-orbit flights; the remaining four were to be modified to permit missions up to 27 hours in length—a total of 18 orbits, exceeding slightly the time spent in space by Titov.

NASA announced immediately after the Glenn flight that the plan was to maintain a steady schedule of manned flights in Project Mercury, that our astronauts would all have the opportunity to make the orbital missions, and that these would take place once every 60 days.

The intentions were admirable, but anyone who experienced at close hand the problems of delays, postponements, and scrubs with Project Mercury should have known better than to forecast so ideal a schedule.

The only launch pad at Cape Canaveral capable of launching the Mercury capsule was Complex Fourteen, and the time requirements of capsule checkout, booster checkout, booster-capsule mating, and then the long countdown plainly overtax the capabilities of NASA and the Cape facilities for the one-flight-every-two-months plans.

On this basis, the Mercury-Atlas 7 should have been on the pad and ready for orbital flight by April 20, 1961. But this was far beyond the reality of the situation, and soon after Glenn's flight it became obvious that the next capsule wasn't going anywhere until mid-May at the earliest.

The results of Glenn's flight also dictated immediate changes and improvements in the Mercury capsule. The small microswitch that caused the erroneous heat-shield release signal was removed from the capsule entirely, and replaced with another microswitch from a different manufacturer.

A major modification was made to the reaction jet system. In the *Friendship 7* capsule the pinpoint orifices of the one-pound jet thrusters (in right yaw) became clogged. Engineers removed these and replaced them with a baffle arrangement intended specifically to eliminate the clogging problem.

How many three-orbit flights are to be made following the Mercury-Atlas 6 and Mercury-Atlas 7 missions? This is a question that can't be answered without additional data—the problem of "one flight is a miracle; two is statistical." NASA in late May still had three capsules assigned to three-orbit missions, but during June, assigned Astronaut W. M. Schirra to a six-to-seven-orbit mission, with a Pacific Ocean landing near either Midway or Honolulu. L. Gordon Cooper became Schirra's backup for the MA-8 flight.

Brainerd Holmes, Director of Manned Space Flight for NASA, explained that NASA planned "several other three-orbital flights, but whether we do them or not depends on how successful we are with and how much we learn from MA-7." He stressed that NASA had "scheduled two other three-orbital shots in addition to MA-7. We also plan an 18-orbital flight at the turn of the year. . . ." Apparently, MA-7 was a "smashing success."

Holmes (in May, 1962) explained that at this stage of evaluating the Glenn flight, NASA had not yet made its decision in terms of a flight of about seven orbits, but that the space agency was giving "serious consideration" to the possibility. An extended mission of this type would mean that the astronaut "would probably land in the Pacific from a six- or seven-orbit mission." However, not even Carpenter's flight was sufficient to allow NASA to make an immediate decision on the seven-orbit mission. The decision finally came in June.

Holmes added that there was good reason to plan on such a flight. The astronaut would receive "more than twice as much weightlessless as from three orbits." He stressed the problems experienced by Titov and that "we would like to know more about that problem."

For the 18 orbits in space, the Mercury capsule will be extensively modified. Glenn proved beyond question the ability of a man to control his systems in orbit; that proof affected immediately the second flight. In MA-7, explained Astronaut M.

Scott Carpenter, the flight plan called for the mission "to be one controlled manually, with the automatic system being the backup rather than vice versa. The automatic attitude-control system was primary in John's flight and he backed *it* up."

Replacement of an Astronaut

A personnel change—seemingly only a minor news item—hit the Project Mercury program and the United States in general like a bombshell in mid-March. Even before Glenn orbited the earth, with M. Scott Carpenter as his backup pilot, the news was out that the astronaut for the following shot, MA-7, would be Donald K. "Deke" Slayton. Walter M. Schirra was assigned as the backup pilot to Slayton.

Then came the sudden news that NASA had withdrawn Slayton from his assignment for the orbital flight, and was replacing him with Carpenter. No one newsman caught the undercurrent of dismay resulting from this decision better than William Hines:

> The sudden removal of Donald K. Slayton as America's second orbital astronaut leaves several interesting and disturbing questions unanswered.
>
> Even granting that a change in Major Slayton's status was necessary because of erratic heartbeat—and there is no unanimity of medical opinion on this point—the way the change was effected was curious from the viewpoints of public relations and personnel management.
>
> The cumulative effect of the Slayton affair was to raise questions about the National Aeronautics and Space Administration's selection and examination programs, the "team" philosophy of Mercury flights, the qualifications of certain of the astronauts, and the soundness of some of the decisions taken at the headquarters of the multi-billion-dollar space program. . . .[1]

Slayton's disqualification from MA-7 came only seven weeks before he was scheduled to go into space—and it came as a shock to the astronaut. He managed to present as calm and settled an appearance as was possible at press conferences on the question —which could only be regarded as extraordinarily difficult for

[1] *The Washington Evening Star.*

him—but his feelings were apparent enough. Slayton said flatly that he was "damned disappointed" and that he was "shot out of the saddle unexpectedly."

Slayton's removal was the direct result of a strong recommendation by a panel of cardiologists (both military and civilian) of the Air Force because of a "heart flutter."

Dr. Charles H. Roadman, head of aerospace medicine in NASA's manned space-flight program (Roadman was formerly a brigadier general with the USAF Directorate of Research and Advanced Technology), described Slayton's condition as "paroxysmal adrial fibrillation." Dr. Roadman said this was "a well-known clinical condition," which is manifested at indeterminate times by a fluttering or increased movement of the valves in the upper portion of the heart.

How serious is this condition? Slayton has had it for years. It has never interfered with his work. The occasional erratic beating of his heart, explained Slayton, was first discovered late in 1959 when he was preparing for a centrifuge test. As part of the test he was undergoing an electrocardiograph check.

Dr. William K. Douglas immediately ordered exhaustive examinations of Astronaut Slayton. An outstanding cardiologist stated flatly after his tests that he saw no reason why Slayton should not remain in the program. At the School of Aviation Medicine of the Air Force in Texas, a special panel of heart experts concluded that there were no disabling aspects of Slayton's condition, and they specifically *recommended that he be continued* in the program.

Air Force and civilian experts in both heart conditions and aerospace medicine generally were brought into the picture. Everyone agreed—unanimously—that Slayton continue.

On March 13, 1962, Slayton was notified that a medical board was "re-evaluating his selection" for MA-7. The next day he conferred with officials on the decision to remove him from the orbital flight.

After the decision for removal of Slayton from MA-7 was made, the sorely disappointed astronaut explained that the erratic heartbeats occurred about every two weeks and might last for

two or three days. To eliminate the temporarily erratic beat, Slayton said, "I get rid of them by going out and running for two or three miles." Slayton emphasized the defect was minor, and that it was "like having one brown and one blue eye."

How could the sudden change of attitude and of official evaluation of Slayton's condition come when it did? The condition was known since 1959. Slayton continued his physically demanding work on the centrifuge that imposed severe punishment on his heart and body. He flew jet fighters at supersonic speeds, wore pressure suits, underwent grueling tests and training.

Stress was absolutely no factor in bringing on the erratic heartbeat, and obviously his continued flying in a very high-performance jet fighter plane meant his complete "okay" from Air Force flight surgeons.

But in the weeks prior to and immediately after Glenn's flight, Slayton's condition was brought to the attention of high NASA officials. This seemed unusual since in the preceding two years Slayton had had at least 50 of the heart tremors with no undue results. But *after* Slayton's selection (made in November, 1961) for MA-7, the highest official of NASA ordered a thorough medical review.

Could NASA make the review—*shouldn't* NASA make that medical review? No, it seemed—for Slayton was an Air Force major, and because he is a commissioned military officer, he came under Air Force jurisdiction. Which seems a strange conflict of authority in terms of the insistence upon the totally "civilian nature" of the astronaut program. Strange or not, that decision stuck, and an Air Force medical review board made up of miliary and civilian doctors handed down their decision.

"Remove Slayton from MA-7."

Considered by many as an "extraordinarily capable" pilot, Deke Slayton (top) was assigned to pilot MA-7 capsule in three orbits; his backup pilot was Marty Schirra (center). But strange twist entered NASA policy when a medical board ruled that a minor heart flutter disqualified Slayton from MA-7. As backup, Schirra should have become new prime pilot. Instead, NASA assigned Scott Carpenter (below), who was Glenn's backup, to become MA-7 astronaut, and later assigned Schirra to a six-orbit flight.

The decision was a thunderbolt in more ways than one, and it left a ringing discord clamoring throughout NASA headquarters. First, the board was *not* unanimous. Second, and much more important, top NASA authorities most closely associated with the astronauts disagreed vehemently on the removal order. Dr. Hugh Dryden stated flatly: "Let's make it clear. Deke is ready to go as far as I'm concerned."

Robert Gilruth specified that ". . . my own feeling is that Deke is an extremely competent engineer-test pilot and entirely capable of the mission. In no case has the abnormality interfered with Deke's performance."

Dr. Douglas has disagreed most strongly with the decision.

But as things turned out, Secretary of the Air Force Eugene M. Zuckert felt sufficiently alarmed about the panel recommendation to go directly to NASA Administrator James E. Webb. And Webb ordered Slayton removed.

Brainerd Holmes, the NASA manned space-flight director, stated that he takes the responsibility for the final decision within NASA.

One of the immediate results of the decision—staged as it was against the backdrop of sharp conflict and disagreement between the officials involved—was evidence that the tightly knit Mercury program was beginning to shred in terms of its central authority. That the astronauts' personal physician, the project director, the operations director, the medical director, and others should all be overruled at the "last moment" by the judgment of a board, many of whose members did *not* work in the aerospace field, came as a blow that is still having its effects within NASA.

There seems hardly any question but that the decision made so quickly had behind it public relations factors equal to, and likely exceeding, the medical findings involved. If there was a failure in the flight—even if the Atlas blew up on the pad with the astronaut just waiting for the launch to start, explained a NASA official—the public was almost certain to blame NASA for allowing a "man with a heart ailment" to be assigned to the mission.

Whatever the arguments—in terms of MA-7, Slayton was out,

and Carpenter was in. What was Carpenter's reaction to his sudden selection? He did not like "to be part of something of such great disappointment to Deke." He added: "But someone has to take it, and I'm glad I had the opportunity to take over from him and make the flight."

Carpenter's selection in itself posed a serious question in respect to the Mercury program. That program has been so set up that if anything happened to remove a primary pilot from a space mission, his backup—who was in many respects his "alter ego"—moved in to take his place. This has been the heart of the "team" effort.

But *Schirra*—not Carpenter—was the backup to Slayton. And what struck an even more curious—and unanswered—questioning note to the Mercury project was the fact that Schirra, a superbly able and dedicated pilot, was suddenly yanked from his slot and placed in position as the backup pilot to Carpenter.

Dr. Hugh Dryden explained this decision by saying that "it was quicker and easier to use Commander Carpenter than Schirra who has far less experience."

As Bill Hines put it: "What experience, in fact, has the one man had that the other lacks?"

The three astronauts with space experience were Shepard, Grissom, and Glenn. As backup pilot to Glenn, Carpenter certainly was close to the entire MA-6 preparations. But the astronauts have avowed time and again that each man was equally capable, and neither Carpenter nor Schirra had been off the ground in a capsule. Both had trained with the same programs, both were superbly capable in their tasks. And in terms of experience, Shepard and Grissom were both available.

And how does the factor of "experience" dictate Schirra's choice for MA-8—with Shepard and Grissom around?

In the earlier days of the program, NASA made it absolutely clear that for any particular mission, the displacement of the primary astronaut would bring his backup into the prime pilot role. All that NASA has said about this is that the rules were changed, and they were changed on the "high level" of Project Mercury itself. The inevitable question, of course, is whether or not something about Schirra was discovered that prevented him from moving into the pilot's position for MA-7. NASA states flatly that nothing of the sort has happened.

The end result—a big question mark about the personal embarrassment that certainly must have arisen from Schirra's continued position as backup for MA-7. Plus some other questions that have never really been answered, and that leave smoldering behind the scenes the matter of the NASA Mercury medical staff having their rulings ignored, and the Mercury project chief having his right of astronaut selection, for one, taken out of his hands.

The Future of Project Mercury

The "big gun" for Project Mercury has always been a mission of at least one full day in space—a manned orbit for a minimum of 24 hours. The equipment status by the time Glenn's flight was evaluated was cheering in relation to this goal. Of the eight Mercury capsules on hand, NASA was planning to modify four of them for planned missions of 18 orbits, which means some 27 hours of consecutive manned space flight.

Without question, drastic changes were called for in the modification of the 18-orbit capsules. Eight Atlas D-model boosters were on tap for Mercury, and the engineering staff felt it imperative that no new requirement be placed on the booster vehicle. If the Mercury capsule were increased in weight, then the booster programing would change—and this was undesired. So the key to redesign of the Mercury spacecraft was to keep the capsule weight down to what it was for Glenn's flight. At launch, *Friendship 7* weighed 4,265 pounds. A substantial weight was jettisoned (escape tower, escape rocket, jettison rocket, etc.) during the launch phase; the capsule in orbit weighed 2,987 pounds. For a second time the capsule went through weight reduction—in the process of re-entry and landing it shed its retropack, straps, parachutes, recovery aids, and other equipment; the landing weight was down to 2,493 pounds.

Above all, Astronaut Glenn's performance allowed eliminating the concept of the completely automated system in Mercury—

and the redundancy of 100-per-cent backup systems. First to be eliminated from the capsule was the 80-pound periscope, the use of which was found during Glenn's flight to be much less important than had been believed.

To eliminate weight in other areas, NASA engineers redesigned the capsule in order to remove (in addition to the periscope) the sonar system (explosive charges released after the capsule lands; the bombs sink before exploding; ships "home" on the blasts to find the capsule); one radio command receiver; one backup recovery beacon; one backup UHF (Ultra High Frequency) radio; and one of the two telemetry systems in the vehicle.

They added 14 pounds more of batteries, 50 per cent more oxygen supply and tankage, and more coolant water.

Weightlessness Studies

Despite the overwhelming success enjoyed by John Glenn and Scott Carpenter in terms of their reaction to almost five hours of weightlessness in the MA-6 and MA-7, the problems of man's exposure to extended zero gravity are still far from solution. As long as were Glenn and Carpenter in orbit, they had each only about one-twentieth of the weightless flight reached by Nikolayev. And we are only scratching the surface of weightlessness and man's reactions to this unusual state in our own space program.

The very nature of the Soviet bioastronautics program, with its renewed emphasis upon biological studies under zero gravity, is a major indication that many hurdles remain here to be crossed. The fact that Titov's problems existed, and that he was a superb physical specimen, a combat jet pilot, and, perhaps even more important, one of the outstanding athletes of the USSR (he was awarded the Master of Sport medal by the Russian government, a major achievement in that country), all point to possibly serious physiological barriers in terms of life under extended weightlessness, in terms of weeks in space.

The Aerospace Medical Association stresses the fact that there remain grave unknowns in terms of how the human body will react to "long-term gravity-free states." The doctors of this group point out—as have the Russians with increasing emphasis—that mechanical aids or even drugs may prove eventually to be necessary for long space flights, in order to assist the astronaut in overcoming the more serious problems of extended weightlessness.

Titov ate three full meals in space, and Major Nikolayev ate in space for four days. But none of these men has been in space long enough for us to discover the true effects upon the digestive system, and the movement of food through the stomach, of the weightlessness condition.

To move food through the human digestive tract, the body undergoes wavelike muscular contractions (peristalsis). These act to move the food in the direction and at the speed the body needs for the processes of digestion. And this takes place under zero gravity as well as it does on the earth, from all indications.

But a problem arises in the fact that the upper part of the stomach acts as a food reservoir—a storage area for food that is not required immediately for digestion. What happens under zero gravity for several days? Without the familiar downward pull of gravity, will the body be able to pull this food downward into the digestive tract—or will it remain in its "storage area"? We don't know—and won't—until we have men in space for many weeks and perhaps even months. Doctors then might find it advisable to administer to the astronauts drugs that would stimulate the peristalsis activity of the body.

Medical research of this nature—plus "mechanical aids" such as slow rotation of a spacecraft—may prove indispensable to the future of man in space.

It is along avenues such as these that NASA will travel in its manned space-flight program in the future.

The true starting point for the "breakaway" was the orbital flight of John Glenn when, in the astronaut's own words:

"We have piped man aboard as the pilot of spacecraft. Now we can get rid of some of that automatic equipment and let man take over."

XI: *Project Gemini*

SEVERAL DAYS BEFORE John Glenn left the earth for his three orbits of this planet, the National Aeronautics and Space Administration issued an official statement on the future of Project Mercury. It was almost as if NASA were closing the door on Mercury before its first goal was reached, but the expressions were directed toward the future role of the man-in-space program.

Manned space flight comes of age [stated NASA] as the NASA Manned Spacecraft Center's Project Mercury—America's initial step into space—approaches its end. Actively participating in this new age is Man, presently led by the Nation's seven astronauts, given the part by organization of NASA on October 1, 1958.

. . . Mercury has been a difficult but inspiring, vastly informing and rewarding task. In the short time since its official inception, the project has passed through stages of research, development, engineering, design, manufacture, and unmanned and manned ballistic flight tests.

Thus, the project nears its conclusion with the coming manned orbital flight. Man's capability in the once alien environment of space is being confirmed. More ambitious undertakings, including manned exploration of space and the distant planets, can now be performed.

[Reading this on Cape Canaveral as we sweated out one scrub after the other, and the repeated postponements, made that last sentence seem just a bit premature. M.C.]

Accomplishments to date, though, include more far-reaching areas than just the Mercury spacecraft.

One of these areas is expanded, solid management capability for conduct of manned space flight research activity. The Manned

Spacecraft Center—with a large co-operative support organization composed of a sizable segment of the Department of Defense, civilian industry, scientific and research organization[s],
and elements of the entire NASA—now represents a major management source.

A second area includes developed and expanded industrial
knowhow and capacity for design and manufacture of very complex spacecraft and related systems. . . .

Therein lies the key to the future of our manned space effort—
the tremendous organization already established, prime for continued growth and expansion, and all of it extraordinarily well
blooded as a result of the Glenn and Carpenter flights.

That organization has been working since December 7, 1961,
on the outgrowth of Project Mercury—Project Gemini, the program to develop and orbit a two-man spaceship, to effect rendezvous and docking maneuvers in space, to develop new methods
of landing from space, and to lay the groundwork through hard-
and-fast experience in space for Project Apollo—our effort to
land several men safely on the surface of the moon before this
decade is out.

From its very inception Project Mercury has been a program
with a "dead end." It was never intended to produce a spaceship
capable of any activities in orbit other than to prove out systems,
and especially to establish the limitations and capabilities of the
human crew member in the environment of space.

We have already seen that the very first orbital flight of an
astronaut in the Mercury spacecraft produced, unexpectedly,
dividends far greater than any of us could have anticipated.

Mercury is the test vehicle, the tentative probe. Before Mercury passes from existence after its seven-orbit and 18-orbit
flights, it will have opened the door wide to Gemini.

Mercury was the start, Gemini is the framework, and Apollo
is the first real end result in this country's manned space effort
in terms of flight away from the immediate vicinity of our planet

Not too long ago Gemini did not exist. Indeed, the three-man
Apollo spaceship program was already on its way nearly two
years before Gemini became officially authorized as a specific
NASA effort. Gemini, one might say, is a product directly of the

John Glenn undergoes medical examinations after his return to earth from his spectacular three orbits. (Above) Glenn in peripheral vision test. (Below) The astronaut sits patiently as doctors place electrodes on his head for detailed tests.

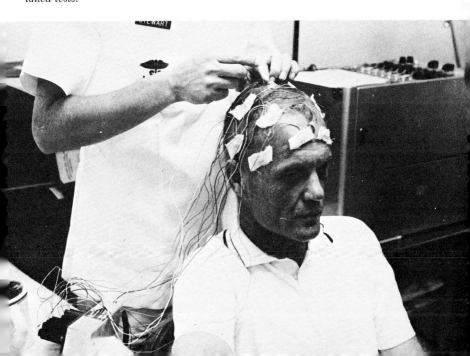

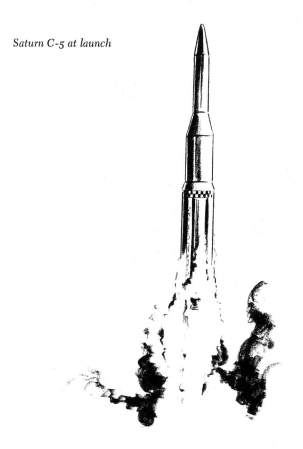

Saturn C-5 at launch

demonstrated needs of research in space and, as such, it is being regarded as an ambitious undertaking with tailor-made plans in mind.

Gemini is, in effect, a bridge from the present across a gulf of unknown quantities to a demonstrated goal—men on the moon.

When Project Apollo first came into being, our concept for flight to the moon involved a direct route. An enormous Nova-type booster would ram a heavy spaceship out of the atmosphere and fling it on its course toward the moon. That spaceship would consist of several *modules*—the spaceship, the spaceship propulsion-control system, the propulsion system to land on the moon, and the propulsion system with which to embark from the lunar surface.

The "first Saturn." Fired in October of 1961, its flight was a spectacular
success (as was the second test in early 1962). The enormous rocket weighed
nearly 1,000,000 pounds and generated 1,300,000 pounds thrust. Saturn C-1
will carry a ten-ton payload into a low orbit of the earth.

But "direct ascent" is a problem of monumental proportions. Was there some means of eliminating some of those probems—even temporarily—by reducing the immediate need for the giant Nova booster of 12,000,000 pounds thrust in the first stage alone?

There was. *If* means could be worked out to effect a maneuver known as "rendezvous and docking" in space, then it would be possible to dispatch the same size lunar vehicle on its way to the distant moon by using boosters of far less power than the Nova first stage.

We could not afford to wait until the giant rocket boosters for Apollo were ready for their first test flights. The enormous Saturn C-1, with eight first-stage motors and 1,500,000 pounds thrust, dwarfing anything else in the country, was already in its early test-flight phase. But not even Saturn C-1, which can send in a single shot a 20,000-pound spaceship into orbit about the earth, is nearly powerful enough for the lunar missions. The "advanced Saturn"—the C-5 model—would be ready by 1966 or 1967 for flight. This monster, with five Rocketdyne F.1 motors as its first stage, could send into orbit about the earth with one firing a payload of 200,000 pounds! The five F.1 motors combined produce a thrust of 7,500,000 pounds.

In the period of time that the enormous boosters are being developed, the United States must determine beyond any question the feasibility of rendezvous, docking, and orbital maneuvers. The Saturn C-1 will be able to launch the three-man Apollo into orbit (ten tons payload) by 1965 if the program goes as planned. Soon afterward the C-5 booster will be on its launch pad.

If we are going to make it to the moon's surface with men by the end of the decade—perhaps even by 1967–68 if we are to believe the time forecasts of NASA—then work must be conducted simultaneously to *perfect* the rendezvous techniques.

It cannot be done with Project Mercury. The capsule is too small, too cramped, and was never designed with this type of operation in mind.

But several years will pass between the final goals of Mercury and the initial flights of Apollo. A bridge is needed, and badly.

That bridge is . . . Gemini, named for the twin stars, Castor and Pollux.

Gemini is in every respect an ambitious undertaking, a hard-driving program with specific and meaningful goals. It is intended to give us a true manned capability in space of performing various tasks and missions, so that our astronauts will be able to function far more extensively than the occupant of the Mercury spacecraft.

"The main objectives of the new two-man spacecraft," explains a NASA official, "will be to provide an early means of experimenting with earth-orbital flights of a week or more to study how man functions under prolonged conditions of weightlessness and to carry out a variety of scientific investigations of space that require men to participate and supervise; to carry out manned rendezvous and docking (being brought together) techniques; to provide pilot training for future, long-duration, circumlunar, and lunar-landing missions; and to provide, later, supply and crew transfer, and maintenance and rescue."

The Gemini Spaceship

In its external configuration, it will be difficult to distinguish between the Mercury and Gemini spaceships—at least in their orbital configuration. Gemini, like its predecessor, is a bell-shaped capsule. But the differences, while not obvious to the eye, will be extensive.

Gemini weighs approximately twice as much as Mercury, with present plans indicating the weight in orbit at 6,000 pounds. Externally, the Gemini will be about a foot higher and a foot wider than Mercury—on the order of a 20-per-cent increase in size. While this may not seem to be very extensive, even this slight increase results in a 50-per-cent increase in the interior *volume* of the spacecraft, making Gemini a cramped, but practicable two-man vehicle for orbital flights up to two weeks in duration.

(As a one-man spaceship with a modified interior, Gemini could orbit an astronaut for a three-week period. NASA does not,

The two-man Gemini spaceship compared to Mercury. Gemini is about one foot wider and two feet higher than Mercury, with 50 per cent greater internal space (relative dimensions not shown here). In orbit, Gemini will weigh 6,000 pounds and will be able to sustain two men in space for a week. It will be used to check out rendezvous and docking techniques. The booster is Titan II.

however, plan for such extended solo flights in which the man must remain, essentially, within the small confines of the Gemini interior. With all the improvement in size involved with Gemini, it is still much smaller and lighter than the early-model *Vostoks*, which are approximately 22 feet in length, 12 to 14 feet in width, and which weigh over 10,000 pounds.)

Within Gemini the two men lie in a side-by-side position, each with major controls and instruments before him. But the true design philosophy of Gemini is not readily apparent, despite its great departure from the Mercury systems.

Scientists will experience much less difficulty and certainly much less time lost during the extensive capsule checkouts at Cape Canaveral. Since Gemini has the exact, albeit slightly enlarged, external configuration of Mercury, technicians should feel "right at home" working on the new spaceship. But at least the ease with which it may be checked out and repaired is entirely new.

Gemini takes advantage of every lesson learned in Mercury; thus, it takes the best and most reliable equipment of the one-man spaceship and adapts it for use with the two-man vehicle. The Mercury spacecraft communication system, the environmental-control system, and many other items are identical to those of Mercury.

The major changes involve the placement of this equipment within Gemini. Inside capsules like *Friendship 7* and *Aurora 7,* the necessary equipment is crammed into the capsule in layers, one atop the other, packed tightly within the interior. Gemini uses much of this same equipment—perhaps even more when it reaches its operational stage—except that the equipment is housed in two main bays that are outside the pressurized interior section of the capsule. The equipment lies within the heat protection of the capsule body, but it is not directly inside that separate, pressurized, and sealed "biological unit" of Gemini.

A change of this nature means a savings of many weeks, perhaps even months, in the checkout-procedure time requirements of spacecraft at Cape Canaveral. The bays can be opened, the equipment is readily accessible, and checkouts and modifications are made with a minimum of trouble.

"These changes are important," explains Brainerd Holmes, "for they will allow us to put manned space flight on more of an operational basis, as opposed to the research and development effort that is involved in Project Mercury. They are the same changes that are generally found when we compare a first prototype aircraft with its later production version."

NASA is convinced that two men are needed in space for the rendezvous maneuver—they feel this will lie beyond the capability of one man (although the Russians may disagree)—and bioastronautics doctors are insistent that a man alone in space should not be called upon to operate his craft for more than one full day in any time period. He must have someone else "take over" for a while if he is to retain efficiency in his work—and there is very, very little room for error "out there."

Brainerd Holmes emphasizes that "the external shape of the Gemini craft will be identical to the Mercury craft."

This factor alone is of vital importance in getting the Gemini program into "action" as quickly as possible. Gemini is only ten inches wider in diameter across the base than Mercury and the aerodynamic characteristics of both are the same. Thus Gemini comes into existence with all that NASA has learned about re-entry, stability, and other factors applying fully to the new spaceship. Gemini eliminates in this area alone many thousands of tests in wind tunnels, with models, with air drops, and with rocket-boosted vehicles.

The concept of the "shelving arrangement" of equipment for Gemini will in itself contribute greatly to the final end-design in Apollo. The layout of equipment in Gemini—called "modular arrangement"—means that engineers will develop new equipment and subsystems for flight tests in Gemini that will later be applied directly to the Apollo spaceship—again cutting off time in completing the development requirements to reach the moon. Gemini may eventually mean a saving of one to three years in reaching the surface of the moon, in its role as a flying testbed for Apollo components and as an astronaut trainer.

Gemini may in time become known as the greatest "headache saver" of our manned space effort. First, it enables us to

First Titan II missile test on March 16, 1962, was a "solid success," as the 103-foot giant thundered from Cape Canaveral on the beginning of a 5,000-mile flight. The 150-ton rocket has 430,000 pounds thrust in the first stage, 100,000 pounds thrust in the upper stage. It will boost a three-ton Gemini into orbit.

benefit from every lesson of Mercury and, second, it is large enough and sufficiently flexible to allow us to use past experience as "building blocks of new procedures."

For example, each Mercury flight meant the recording aboard the capsule of enormous quantities of flight data during the mission. To reduce and evaluate this information, and to prepare the voluminous reports on each mission, has been a tedious, costly, and time-consuming operation. Through improved data-gathering techniques and procedures this problem is being eliminated.

In Gemini, the scientists are using equipment which prints data only for those periods of Gemini flight during which systems operations and events occur beyond the planned limits of the mission. This doesn't reduce the vital over-all knowledge of the mission progress, for during the flight full information will continue to be transmitted over telemetry channels to ground receiving stations.

As mentioned previously, Gemini does not have the high escape tower and rocket that so clearly marks the Mercury spacecraft atop its booster. Following the principle of design in the *Vostoks*, ejection seats are built right into the vehicle to provide the two pilots with "explosively actuated escape" on the pad, during powered ascent or during descent.

In its early flights the Gemini spacecraft will return to earth much the same way as did the Mercury. As it re-enters the lower atmosphere a drogue parachute will be ejected to stabilize the spaceship. Then, about 10,000 feet high, the main parachute will open—an enormous 96-foot ringsail parachute (33 feet wider than the Mercury parachute system).

But there remains a major difference between Mercury and Gemini. John Glenn and Scott Carpenter had no personal parachutes (Shepard did) in their capsules, and if their spaceship parachutes had failed—well, that would have been the end of the story. This won't be true in the case of Gemini, since the ejection seats provide individual escape and descent protection without the escape tower and rocket. To those of us accustomed to looking at the Mercury-Atlas system across the Cape before

Titan II launch with Gemini

a launch, Gemini will seem to be missing that "certain something!"

The booster for the Gemini spaceship is the new Titan II, successor to the Titan I ICBM. Titan II is a husky giant that will stand well over 110 feet tall with the Gemini spacecraft. Unlike Atlas, Titan II does not use liquid oxygen. Instead, the booster is fueled with a hypergolic fuel, which is self-igniting and contains its own oxidizer. This means that it does not have the critical loxing period prior to launch and that countdowns can be brought right down to the last several seconds, "held" for many minutes, and then the booster can be fired on a split-second scheduling.

The familiar spacesuit worn by the Mercury astronauts is soon to become a "discard" of the rapidly developing exploration of space; a new pressure suit has long been in development for Gemini. One version of the new personal-equipment suits for space has removable arms and legs. These are designed to provide maximum comfort for the astronaut in orbit—and also to

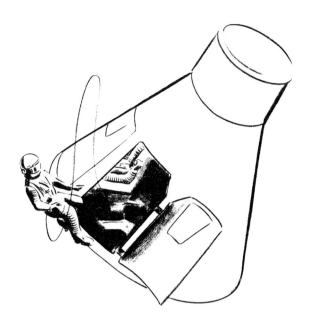

Gemini astronauts in orbit, working on spacecraft

allow some physical exercise for the men who may be weightless for several days or a week at a time. Doctors are concerned that the sustained zero-gravity condition will cause adverse effects unless the astronaut makes certain to exercise his muscles. After a week under weightlessness, for example, return to the atmosphere and the deceleration forces of re-entry will hit the man with all the force of a piledriver. Without careful preparations for this, he may become temporarily dizzy. This is not permanently harmful, except that the man cannot afford even a moment's dizziness during the critical time of re-entry.

The Gemini program also calls for the men—in the later stages of the orbital flights with the two-man spaceship—to leave their vehicle for work on the external surfaces of the ship, and to practice the docking maneuvers and equipment handling with other spacecraft. This will require the development of what NASA terms an "extra-vehicular" suit; this project has long been under way with a number of firms.

Joe Schmitt, suit technician for the astronauts, explains that the primary function of the suit now in use is to withstand internal pressure forces of five pounds per square inch (factory tests are made at 7.5 psi). The greatest problem with the suit in Mercury is leakage (which cannot be higher than 250 cubic centimeters per minute); the most critical point of leakage has been the seal around the clear Plexiglas visor.

"One of our regular tests is to inflate the visor seal bladder and then disconnect the hose and let it stand overnight," explains Schmitt. "It should remain inflated that long."

The suit technician stresses that the zippers on the suit and the stitching around them are a particular source of reliability headaches. "When we're looking for a specific point of leak, we rub a sort of liquid soap around the visor seal and any other suspected opening. Escaping air then blows bubbles in the mixture, neatly pinpointing the leak."

Suit inspections—to become even more critical in the Gemini program because of extended times in space and perhaps movement away from the pressurized protection of the capsule—already involve turning the suits inside out and checking each and every seam in visual inspections prior to the pressure checks. Within each suit 15 feet of ventilation tubing must all be inspected. Microphones and helmet earphones are checked, and the helmet visor must be clear of all scratches. Blood pressure and bio-instruments, which measure pulse rate, heartbeat, respiration, and other in-flight medical data, must be exhaustively checked out.

Even the most careful preparations cannot prevent errors. "One problem in particular that cropped up with Glenn's suit," Schmitt said, "was the left wrist bearing seal. It had a high leak rate at low pressure. We found it had been installed backwards."

Schmitt explained some suit developments: "We've gone through many small changes to increase the mobility of the suit, especially around the shoulders. And of course there are a number of accessories that we add from time to time according to the preference of the astronaut. For instance, he can have two wrist mirrors, a flat one and a parabolic mirror, to assist in reading the instruments behind his head.

"And there are other changes contemplated. The Mercury suit, which is an adaptation of the Navy's Mark IV pressure suit, has a long zipper slanting from one shoulder to the opposite hip. Counting the underwear—the longjohns—boots, helmet, gloves, and suit, it takes about 20 minutes to dress the astronaut. The suit planned for Project Gemini will have a horseshoe-shaped zipper running from one shoulder down to the stomach and back up to the other shoulder. It should make dressing easier."

Backing up the demand for more crewmen for space shots, NASA has brought new astronauts into the manned space program, with ten pilots chosen in the "second astronaut selection." The age requirements for the new "team" specified a maximum age limit of 35, a height of six feet, and a weight of 190 pounds.

Civilian pilots for the first time were eligible for the program. The requirements from NASA were: a degree or its equivalent in the biological sciences or engineering; several thousand hours of flying time, plus extensive recent jet time; and a test-pilot rating obtained through NASA, the military services, or through industry.

(By 1968 NASA will need a force of at least 21 astronauts; additional selections are planned during 1964 and 1965 for the lunar landing missions.)

During the announcement that more astronauts were being sought, the question came up of women astronauts. NASA Administrator James Webb said that he did not believe there were many women with the required test-flight experience.

"I do not think that we will be anxious to put a woman or any other person of particular race or creed into orbit just for the purpose of putting them there," he said.

A newsman asked Glenn: "We hear a number of women want to get into the program. What have you to say to this?"

Glenn grinned broadly. "Yeah, how about that?"

Then, in response to the question: "I doubt very much if the women test pilots we know have sufficient time logged in jet aircraft."

The current seven astronauts will serve as Senior Pilots for the Gemini program; the new astronauts will serve as copilots. NASA expects their training to be completed in time for the Gemini missions.

Rendezvous with Gemini—the Plan

Let us assume the time is early 1964. The Gemini project has been actively in operation for nearly a year, and a rendezvous and docking mission is about to get under way.

On Complex Nineteen, along the Canaveral beach, a powerful Titan II booster rears high over the shoreline. Atop the two-stage rocket is the shape of the Gemini capsule, a giant television tube lying on its wide end. The capsule is clear and sharp against the blue sky, framed neatly without the once-familiar tower and escape rocket of Mercury.

But on this morning Titan II will not fly. The two astronauts of the Gemini spaceship are on the ground, closer to the line of Atlas launch complexes. The star of the show this morning is Atlas-Agena B, a husky booster that plays a special role in the Gemini program. Atlas-Agena B is an old and familiar vehicle here on Canaveral; it has launched Samos, Midas, and other satellites; it has sent Rangers to the moon, Mariners to Venus.

The scene is familiar. The upper portion of the Atlas is covered with brilliant ice from the lox tanks, vapor plumes from the vent valves. Then, suddenly, the bluish-white vapors vanish. The valves are closed, the tanks sealed and pressurized as the countdown reaches zero. The verniers spit flame, followed by the volcanic gush of fire from the three main engines. Shackles fly back, and the rocket thunders into the sky.

Many minutes later, after Atlas has disappeared, Agena B is in orbit. For the next 20 hours or more, every detail of that orbit is measured with painstaking care. Information from optical trackers, radar scanners, and telemetry signals are fed into rows of computers. The orbit, velocity, inclination, apogee, perigee—everything about the orbit is measured down to the finest degree.

Technicians feed more problems into the computer. Hours later, the Gemini project director has the information he needs. His requirement is to fire the Titan II booster so that the Gemini space capsule with its two astronauts will be inserted

Gemini spaceship will rendezvous with Agena satellite, shown here as upper stage of Atlas-Agena-B rocket used to launch Ranger moon payloads.

into its own orbit at a precise moment not only in time, but in space as well. When the Gemini moves away from its own booster rocket, in free fall, it must be within close proximity to the Agena B. It must be moving along the same plane so that the two satellites—one a robot and the other manned—do not drift apart. Their angle of orbit in terms of perigee and apogee must be the same. Their velocities must be close.

The information is in; the exact moment to launch Gemini is known.

That night the countdown for the manned flight begins. It is a countdown much shorter than we have known before. The capsule checkout requires much less time, thanks to the new system of "shelf arrangements" and automatic checkout equipment within the Gemini.

The Titan II booster has been fueled for several days. There will be no period as the morning approaches when the signal is given to prepare for the final minutes of the countdown. Things move in a strangely different, wonderfully efficient manner. No rows of trucks filled with liquid oxygen drive up to the launch stand. There is no cooldown of the plumbing, no shrill screaming of the pipes, no vapor plumes, no topping off—none of the signs that marked the countdown of Atlas.

Within Titan II's stages is a hypergolic fuel. The fuel is self-igniting (and so the familiar igniter system is absent from this booster). The oxidizer is within the fuel itself, and so long as pressure is built up within the tanks and the pumps are ready to operate, the fuel (50 percent each of dimethylhydrazine and hydrazine, plus nitrogen tetroxide) will blaze into fire the moment it comes into contact in the combustion chamber.

On the morning of firing, the booster stands ready. Around the other side of the world, Agena B sweeps around the planet, rushing closer and closer. It plunges through space, then soars close to Canaveral, 130 miles above the earth.

The firing command rings out in the blockhouse. Titan II comes alive with startling, explosive suddenness. From the curving flame bucket the steam howls outward, tinged with a bright yellow color.

The booster pushes away from the earth—but there is no

familiar cascade of fire as we have seen so many times in the past. The flame is almost transparent, more pink than red, and there is very little smoke—the characteristic burning of the hypergolic fuel. But through binoculars the shock-wave patterns in the flame are very clear.

This first stage is powerful—430,000 pounds thrust slam sound waves hard against the Canaveral area. Despite the great weight—more than 150 tons—of the booster system, the rocket rushes upward with startling speed. Soon the glare is a pinpoint, and then it winks out completely—invisible now to our sight.

The booster bends more and more toward the horizontal. High above the earth, in space, the first-stage fuel is exhausted. Valves snap closed, combustion dies with a shriek. Then, another explosion in the abrupt silence. The single motor—100,000 pounds thrust—of the upper stage crashes into life. The g forces that had fallen off begin once again to build up against the bodies of the two men, lying side by side in the Gemini capsule.

The second-stage booster accelerates with tremendous speed. Long seconds later, its flame creating an enormous billowing and filmy cloud of ionized gases, the desired speed is reached. The engine shuts down. Posigrade rockets fire to separate the capsule from the empty, useless booster. The capsule edges ahead of the Titan II upper stage.

Gemini is in orbit at 18,000 miles per hour. The Agena satellite is slightly higher than Gemini, 12 miles ahead of the manned capsule. Immediately the two astronauts receive confirmation of their own orbit from the tracking stations below. Computers work full speed to supply additional data in relation to both orbits—Gemini and Agena.

Inside the Gemini spaceship radar equipment locks on to its target—the unmanned satellite. The astronauts peer through angled windows that provide excellent visibility of the area of space before the spaceship. The Agena is clearly visible, and a brilliant flashing light on the surface of the satellite assures that it will remain visible to the astronauts when it—and Gemini —swing around into the dark side of earth.

Gemini has "translational rockets" for its rendezvous maneu-

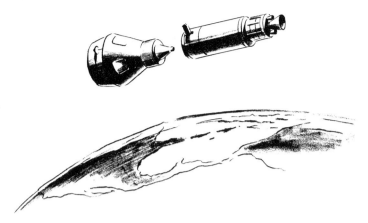

Gemini rendezvous with Agena D

vers. But these are not yet fired. The astronauts receive additional reports from the earth stations. The computers have shown that for the Gemini to close in to Agena, the maneuvers will require an excessive consumption of fuel.

But inside Agena—which has a restart capability in orbit—there is still a great quantity of fuel. The ground stations flash commands to the robot brain of the satellite. Reaction jets position Agena exactly as desired. Then valves flip open and fuel explodes in the combustion chamber of the Agena rocket motor. The satellite decelerates slightly, edges just a bit down in its earth orbit. The differences are very small in terms of earth orbit, but they are extremely—critically—important in terms of the two vehicles in space and their relative positions.

Again the computers display their answers. Gemini and Agena are much closer now. The astronauts work as a superb team. They establish a new attitude of the spaceship. Handling their controls with great sensitivity, they fire their translational rockets.

Slowly the two satellites drift toward one another. Brief bursts of power bring them closer and closer. Now the critical moment is at hand. The astronauts manipulate their power controls rapidly, surely, carefully.

Gemini eases slowly but smoothly into an adapter extending from the Agena. Contact is made. Again the reaction jets spurt their gases. The contact now is more certain; then, it is secure. Gemini and Agena are latched together, a solid joining.

The two have been "docked in orbit." The astronauts confirm the connections between the two space vehicles. Far below, on earth, the computers are still hard at work, digesting the new information. Data flash through space to the manned vehicle, now also in command of the long Agena satellite.

Reaction jets spurt their gases, and the attitude changes once again. The astronauts count down in their spaceship, and they close a switch. The Agena engine flames into life once more, burning steadily.

When it cuts off, the double-spacecraft system is moving faster than before. It is in a new orbit with a perigee higher than first achieved.

For the next several hours the astronauts practice different maneuvers in space. Then it is time to return.

The locking devices holding the two satellites together are

Water landings of spacecraft of ballistic type like Mercury and Gemini pose many severe recovery problems, experienced personally by Astronaut Grissom—shown here as he was hauled from the Atlantic. Grissom was physically exhausted and near drowning when he was pulled from ocean. The rescue harness around his body is on backwards; Grissom said it couldn't have mattered less at this point. In the future, the astronauts will land in the desert . . . maybe with the results shown on the opposite page.

Unshaven, unkempt, unwashed, but none the worse for wear . . . the seven Mercury astronauts after being left in the desert—each man alone— for four days. The purpose was to verify survival techniques, using only the equipment contained within the capsule. They fashioned tents and turbans from parachutes, and followed other special techniques to survive the fierce desert heat. From left to right, our bearded astronauts are Cooper, Carpenter, Glenn, Shepard, Grissom, Schirra, and Slayton. The printed card pinned into Glenn's turban reads: NOT SUITABLE FOR FLIGHT USE. *And how, it's not!*

released. Gemini eases away slowly from the Agena. A brief burst of power, and the two spacecraft begin to drift farther apart, actually in separate, diverging orbits now.

Ground stations track the Gemini orbit for a final sweep around the planet. Data flash to the astronauts in their spacecraft. They position the spacecraft to its retrofire attitude. Over the Pacific Ocean, far to the west of the United States, the retros blaze in vacuum. Gemini begins to fall toward earth; as it starts its long, flat re-entry maneuver, the retropack is jettisoned and retro-attitude is assumed.

The descent by now is familiar—a dozen men have already been through re-entry in both the Mercury and Gemini programs, some of them more than once.

Gemini falls into the denser atmosphere, over California. The

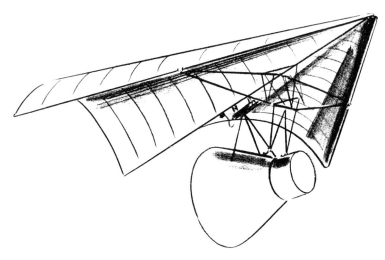

Gemini with Rogallo wing

mountains loom high now, no longer wrinkles on the earth's surface as they were from space. The desert floor stretches flat—especially the long dry lakebed of Muroc, near Edwards Air Force Base.

The small stabilization drogue chute extends, slows the capsule, and dampens out the oscillations. Then an explosive mortar fires, releasing the chute.

An enormous, batlike wing begins to unfold from Gemini— a strange parawing that spreads out to 45 feet in diameter. It is pointed at its front end, sweeping back sharply. The leading edges of the wing scoop in air and fill out for added aerodynamic lift. The entire wing flexes and heaves as if it were alive . . . and no longer does Gemini fall. Instead it cleaves the air like an airplane, its compact fuselage suspended by slim but strong lines beneath the huge, flexing wing high above.

Inside the spacecraft, the astronauts work new controls. A runner skid extends from beneath their spacecraft. Two outriggers for stability in landing move into position. They are ready for the landing maneuvers.

Like a huge bat dropping from space, the Gemini-flexwing system glides with a deep hiss of air toward the desert. But the lakebed—their target, marked with long lines and flarepots that give off smoke to show the direction of the wind—is eight miles to the left. The wing is flexed deliberately this time through the spacecraft's controls. The bat shape bends, angles its form in the air.

Gemini—riding horizontally in the atmosphere—turns in its descent and heads for the lakebed. The pilots have more than 15 miles of runway, and their landing approach and speed is remarkably like that of the old X-15 rocket-propelled research airplane.

Gemini eases along; the pilots increase the angle of attack of the wing. The spacecraft flares out. The skid touches, throws off a high spray of dust. The ship lurches momentarily to the right; the outrigger takes the impact, steadies the vehicle. Slowing down steadily, moving horizontally across the dry lakebed, Gemini trails a huge, running fountain of dust, and then slides to a halt.

The mission is over—the men are home.

XII : *The Space ASPs*

DARKNESS SETTLES over Cape Canaveral like a heavy mist; as quickly as the night eases its bulk onto the spaceport, the towers of Canaveral rise in their gleaming lights to stand forth brilliantly. It is always a sight at once wonderful and bewitching. The parade of colors, the fingers of steel glittering with red and green and white, with dusky orange and spatters of light shining between strands of cable—all this is the sign of the doorway to the void high above this planet. And sometimes, concerned with all the details of the sleek metal forms on this flattened spit of land, the wonder of what is about us pushes into the background, is accepted for commonplace.

But not during one such evening last February, when Complex Fourteen loomed upward from the shore, embracing both a rocket and its capsule—and the men preparing these instruments for their missions far beyond the reach of our eyes.

On that night I stood on the shores of the Cape, the sounds of the preparations for space muted against the hissing rumble of waves along the level beach. With me was an engineer. At the moment he wore a comfortable sport shirt over slacks—no sign here of a brilliant scientific mind, no uniform with silver eagles on the shoulders, as he customarily appears to the public.

We looked at the great gantry tower, listened to the distant clamorous sounds of metal against metal, the faint whisper of voices carried by the wind.

"One day all this will be unnecessary. One day," he said, "we'll be able to leave this world without struggling so hard for every push into that other world above us.

"Each time we fire a man like this . . . we're acting like ignorant savages at the edge of a stormy beach. Each time we want to go somewhere, we push our way directly into those waves. It's a hard, bitter struggle—and since we lack anything but the crudest of instruments with which to work, we're forced to batter our way through, to slug and push and pound.

"That's the way we fight through gravity. There's nothing smooth or perfected about it. We do it with raw, naked power— we use rockets as battering rams. It's crude and inefficient and terribly wasteful. We do it this way because we have no choice; we don't know any other way yet to get through those breakers—through the gravity that drags us down.

"It's really crude—I mean that. We fire one of these rockets, and they're toys compared to what we're building in things like Nova, and the whole affair of getting into orbit is perilous from the moment someone presses that button to activate the sequencer. The thing goes up vertically; it's a small mountain balanced precariously on a river of fire, the whole thing walking a tightwire of madly spinning gyros—hell, I'm amazed every time we make it.

"We've been lucky so far. We haven't been in the game long enough—or run up against the odds yet—to kill some people. And we're going to do just that. Finally you run out of as much technical reliability as you can, and the odds stick a wrench in the whole flaming works and—*blooey*. A couple of very good people are gone."

He stopped for a moment and looked hard at the gantry. "You know why we push directly into the breakers—into gravity? Because we still haven't learned how to handle ourselves in terms of space. We don't know how to go *over* the breakers.

"We're like the foot soldiers in Napoleon's army. They had to slog their way through everything. They were chained down. Finally someone got the idea of using wings, and suddenly the foot soldier could move fast and hard; he could go over a lot of the obstacles and come down where he wanted. Or maybe the parallel isn't fair in terms of war. It's just as valid in comparing the old wagon trains that crossed the United States to the way we do it now. They used to drag their weary carcasses for months across the mountains and the deserts. Now we go *over* the obstacles, and we do it in a few hours instead of a few months.

"That's how we stand today in space . . . we can't go over, so we go the hardest route. But wouldn't it be nice if we learned how to get up above the ground, and to carry ourselves *over* the breakers—to ease past the gravity barriers? You need energy, except that you're using it in a more efficient manner, and you're cutting down on the risks involved. . . . "

That night we talked about a dream that has one foot well into the door of reality. Engineers call it the *true* spaceship, the ASP.

But ASP is no viper; it stands for *Aerospace Plane*. It's not one design, but the combined result of many hard studies that have been under way for years. It exists in different forms and shapes and plans, but it exists also in some limited hardware form. Engineers are now building and testing some of the components of the ASP.

They call it the *true* spaceship because it "recognizes the facts of life." A vehicle leaving the surface of the earth must first travel through the atmosphere. It must possess the means with which it efficiently moves through the heavy density of the air ocean and, as well, the thin air of the upper atmosphere where hypersonic speeds produce the barrier reefs of shock waves and friction. In space—it must function as a spaceship. Here its external shape is meaningless; since it is a vehicle of centrifugal force, falling around the planet, only its means of *attitude* control are important. But when it returns to the earth, it enters again into the air ocean where aerodynamic forces are of primary—indeed, critical—consideration.

Our spaceships today do not recognize these facts, in terms of most efficiently solving the problems of traversing the different regions. Instead, the spacecraft and its booster and recovery systems we know today are compromises with reality. We can't help that now, and won't be able to change the facts of life for some time.

But if we *could* have that true spaceship—*which has been*

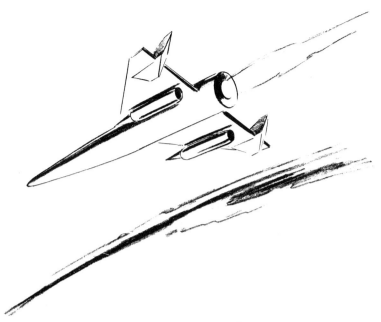

ASP in upper atmosphere

designed, and which is undergoing its early phases of develop-ment—why, we might achieve some truly high levels of space-craft efficiency. ASP takes off as an airplane from a runway—one no longer than that used by the heavy B-52 eight-jet bomber. It uses combinations of power to go higher and faster. Then it scoops up additional fuel from the very substance of the upper atmosphere, shuts down its air-breathing engines, and accelerates under rocket power to its required orbital velocity and height to become a manned spacecraft in orbit. It returns to earth in the re-entry profile, but once in the atmosphere it is automatically of aerodynamic configuration, and it descends under control. It lands as an airplane, to be used again—and again—and as many times as it is deemed ready for flight.

As envisioned by engineers, the military ASP would weigh about 250 tons at takeoff. Its shape would be a canard design—wings swept back so sharply they're called "slashback"—and with the smaller control-stabilizer surfaces at the nose of the vehicle. This isn't anything revolutionary—we've flown planes of this configuration for years, including the ramjet-powered, 2,000-mile-per-hour Navaho missile.

Climbing rapidly, increasing its speed steadily, the ASP soars to high altitude and levels off. Now the speed builds up even higher. As the ASP races along at thousands of miles per hour, it is scooping up the thin air of high altitude. A special system within the ASP compresses the air and liquefies it. Then the equipment separates the oxygen from the nitrogen and pumps the liquid oxygen into fuel tanks. Other tanks are already filled with liquid hydrogen.

And liquid oxygen with liquid hydrogen makes what engineers call a high-energy fuel. By the time the tanks are filled, the ASP weighs some 500 tons—twice as much as when it left its airfield runway. It requires eight times as much liquid oxygen as it does liquid hydrogen to fire the high-energy rocket-motor system—but in this operation the ASP doesn't have to drag the 250 tons of lox up from the surface of the earth. It fills its tanks after it is moving at many thousands of miles per hour and after it is above the greatest percentage and density of the atmosphere.

All this time—should something go wrong—the ASP crew can always abort. This doesn't mean tearing away from the main body of the aircraft (although this safety feature also is included), as we do with our capsules. The machine can always drop down to lower atmosphere and return to a landing field, for another try after repairs.

But if everything works out as planned, soon the lox tanks are full. The fuel tanks are pressurized, the turbopumps started. The air-breathing engines shut down as the rocket motors blaze into life. Accelerating steadily and rapidly, the ASP races upward at a steep angle. Soon it is above the atmosphere, in vacuum. The pilots control the ASP into its required attitude, angle to the earth's surface, and velocity. The motors shut down. ASP is in orbit.

How far from reality is the ASP? It's difficult to hazard any "guesstimates" with this type of system. Even though ASP is the most promising of all aerospace ideas (short of antigravity control), it is also the most complicated and formidable engineering problem we have ever tackled in terms of the conquest of space. Some engineers believe that the perfection of the ASP vehicles will demand engineering solutions to problems that are a hundred times more complex than those faced by scientists when they first decided to build the atomic bomb.

But the author remembers some details about those earlier programs. . . . When the Manhattan Project first started, there were many engineers who estimated that it would probably take at least a century to perfect the nuclear weapon. They were wrong by some 96 years. . . .

Engineers in 1946 and 1947 were absolutely violent when other engineers talked about supersonic flight. Didn't these fools realize there was a sound barrier in the sky, that it was *impossible* to fly faster than the speed of sound? Few people remember those arguments today—when a heavy, four-engine bomber has streaked across the entire continental United States in *two hours.*

The power requirements of ASP truly are formidable. We have power today we never dreamed of before. Engineers are keeping one eye glued to the power source that we have ready for tapping, but have not yet harnessed—nuclear energy—for aircraft propulsion. A nuclear reactor designed specifically for ASP would provide all the energy needed to push the giant machine at thousands of miles per hour through the thin, upper atmosphere. And in space it would also provide a sure, reliable, extended means of power for electrical, communications, and other systems.

The ASP concept may be closer to reality than many people were willing to accept only a few months ago. For more than a year NASA has been studying a replacement for the X-15 rocket airplane—a new research vehicle tentatively labeled the "Super X-15." The title, however, is grossly misleading, for the ASP concept as envisioned by NASA would look nothing like the X-15 and it would enter a wholly new regime of flight performance, including attempts at orbital flight.

Let us review briefly the X-15 role in advancing the concept

of the manned airplane as a bridge to the full ASP vehicle. The X-15 from its outset has been a joint venture of the Air Force, NASA (formerly NACA), the Navy, and the manufacturer—North American Aviation. It was designed to explore the problems and conditions of hypersonic flights (five or more times the speed of sound) up to a speed of 4,400 miles per hour and a maximum altitude of 250,000 feet. It has already exceeded 4,000 miles per hour, and the program now is aiming at altitudes up to 400,000 feet or more. Lt. General Mark Bradley, USAF Deputy Chief of Staff for Systems and Logistics, stated: "Specifically, we will thoroughly investigate the aerodynamic and structural flying qualities of the airplane, and physiological problems of manned flight.

" . . . The X-15 airframe is a midwing monoplane built of inconel X alloy with good high-temperature-strength characteristics. This type of material is required due to the aerodynamic heating of the airplane that occurs in hypersonic flying. Structural temperatures of 1,200° F. are [encountered] . . .

"The aircraft is 50 feet long and has a wingspan of 22 feet. The design launch weight is 31,705 pounds with a weight at burnout of 12,971 pounds, having consumed at a rate of more than 10,000 pounds of fuel per minute. . . . The motor [uses] liquid oxygen as the oxidizer and ammonia as the propellant, and produces 57,000 pounds thrust at flight altitudes. It is designed so that it can be controlled by the pilot and throttled down to 50-per-cent thrust if necessary.

"Pitch and roll control within the atmosphere is obtained by deflection of the horizontal stabilizers, since it does not have conventional ailerons. During ballistic flight above the earth's atmosphere a reaction-control system is used. This control system . . . controls the aircraft in yaw, pitch, and roll with jet nozzles in the wingtips and nose. . . ."

NASA envisions the ASP research aircraft as a vehicle that takes off as an airplane, goes into orbit, and returns from orbit— re-entering and landing as an airplane. It would have a unique power-plant system—three engines in one. This would be a combination turbojet-ramjet-rocket, which already has been tagged with the name of *turboramrocket.*

As designed by NASA, the research vehicle-ASP would be 90 feet long and weigh 50 tons. The wings would be sharply swept back (slashback). The program is estimated as running for ten to 12 years—and would cost at least one billion dollars.

The turbojets would carry the NASA-ASP to a speed of 2,000 miles per hour into the lower stratosphere. There the ram-

X-15 at 300,000 feet

jets would take over, boosting the speed to 6,000 miles per hour and the altitude to between 120,000 and 150,000 feet. At this point the rocket motors take over, sending the NASA-ASP out into space and into orbit.

The X-15 program by itself does not provide the foundation for the ASP project. But in our discussion of ASP—which is at this moment a project under advanced study and components testing only—we have moved ahead of our story. For the bridge between X-15 and ASP *does* exist.

Its name is . . .

Dyna-Soar

The Air Force states of its X-20 Dyna-Soar program:

> This is the most advanced manned aerospace research system now under development by the USAF.
>
> The object of the development is to obtain the technology and demonstrate the capability for manned space flight characterized by the positive recovery of men and equipment from space missions. Such flights will end with landings at typical airbases in a routine, operationally supportable manner and with the inherent reliability of piloted aircraft. The program is a joint USAF-NASA development and test effort, directed and funded by the Air Force. . . .

Dyna-Soar stands for *dynamic soaring*, and sometimes the Dyna-Soar vehicle is described as a *boost-glide aircraft*.

The description is apt—a powerful rocket *boosts* the winged vehicle high above the earth to speeds between 15,000 and 17,000 miles per hour. The vehicle begins its long, very flat return along the edges of the earth's atmosphere. But unlike the Mercury and Gemini spacecraft, Dyna-Soar has wings—and these are efficient lifting surfaces. At tremendous speed Dyna-Soar begins its re-entry. Lift builds up . . . and the vehicle actually *glides* along and through the top of the atmosphere.

Or Dyna-Soar can go into orbit. It decelerates with retro-rockets, re-enters the atmosphere in a long, flattened-out curve. As the speed slows, it begins to drop deeper and deeper into the atmosphere, under pilot control all the way.

The Dyna-Soar has sharply sweptback wings. It looks like an advanced high-speed aircraft, which, in essence, it is. It carries one pilot in its present version, although future models will carry crews of two or more Air Force astronauts.

Dyna-Soar represents a tremendous advance in both aircraft and space-vehicle technology; hence it is that it is described as an aerospace vehicle. It is one of the most unique combinations of aircraft, missile, and satellite technology, since it requires the development of many different systems and techniques —all to take place simultaneously.

Let's look at the booster first—the Titan III. Here again we have a startling departure from the past line of development with our space boosters. Titan III consists of the Titan II booster that will be used for Gemini, but with a vital difference.

Strapped to the sides of the liquid-propellant rocket will be two giant solid-propellant rockets that will function as the first-stage booster.

Titan II has two liquid-propellant motors of 430,000 pounds thrust total in the first stage, and a single motor of 100,000 pounds thrust in the upper stage. This power combination is perfectly capable of meeting the needs of the three-ton Gemini spacecraft, but it is entirely inadequate for Dyna-Soar.

The aerospace vehicle will weigh 15,000 pounds in orbit—a giant among our present spacecraft. It may be compared to the weight of the *Vostok* spaceships used by Gagarin and Titov; these in orbit weighed just over 10,000 pounds.

The solid-propellant boosters for Titan III are each made up of five segments. These are piled one atop the other within a single casing; externally they look just like an ordinary booster, except for their size. Each one of the solid boosters is ten feet in diameter. And with Titan II they form a true powerhouse, for space operations.

The first Titan stage is 70 feet long; the upper stage, about 32 feet. Each of the solid boosters is approximately 70 feet in length (the design may vary before actual flight tests). Here is the boost-phase of the flight:

On the ground, the two solid-propellant boosters fire to begin the launch. Each of these boosters develops 1,350,000 pounds thrust; the tremendous power of 2,700,000 pounds thrust lifts the entire assembly from the launch pad.

The solid boosters, trailing thick plumes of white smoke from the ground, fire for about 100 seconds. Then, as they exhaust their propellants, explosive charges break them free from the Titan booster body. At this moment the main two-engine stage of Titan bursts into flame—and begins to rush into the sky, starting to bend over sharply in the climb.

The main stage burns out. Still attached to the empty booster, the single-engine upper stage fires. The flame vents as long spears of fire through exhaust holes in the clamp ring between the rockets. Then, abruptly, the upper stage pushes away rapidly from the jettisoned booster.

At orbital height and altitude, the upper stage dies out. Small explosive charges separate the Dyna-Soar spaceship. It eases

Titan III launch with Dyna-Soar

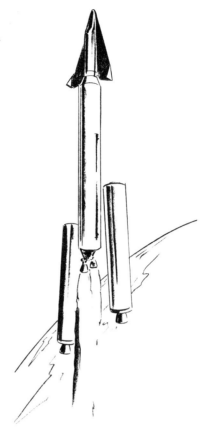

away from the inert booster—in orbit, on its way around the world at nearly 300 miles per minute.

It's possible that the early Titan III flights will not use the 120-inch-wide solid-propellant boosters with their complete five segments. With this arrangement, as described, Titan III has tremendous lift capabilities—it can place a payload of 32,000 pounds into an orbit 170 miles above the earth, which makes it even more powerful in payload-orbit capability than the massive Saturn C-1. If the payload is reduced to 29,000 pounds, Titan III can fire a spaceship into an orbit 350 miles high. Since the first Dyna-Soar vehicles will weigh only 15,000 to 17,000 pounds, it's obvious that a larger version, carrying several men plus extensive equipment, can also be sent into orbit.

Dyna-Soar at insertion into orbit

The Air Force plans to make its first Dyna-Soar orbital mission by late 1964 or early 1965. With a "crash program," the first orbit of Dyna-Soar could come as early as the late summer of 1964.

When the aerospace vehicle returns to the atmosphere in re-entry attitude, it won't come plunging down from space with its nose pointed in the direction of flight. Instead, the pilot will use his reaction jets to place the spaceship into a nose-high attitude. The Dyna-Soar will then be dropping into the atmosphere belly-first—the underside of the vehicle taking the worst brunt of re-entry friction and heating.

To survive the tremendous heat-pulse of re-entry, Dyna-Soar vehicles will make extensive use of molybdenum, columbium, dense graphite, and nickel alloys. These will not only

Dyna-Soar spaceship re-entering atmosphere in high angle of attack attitude

be able to withstand high re-entry temperatures, but they will "reradiate the heat" back into the atmosphere rather than allowing the metal to absorb the great temperatures.

As the Titan boosters are being test-flown and developed at Cape Canaveral, the Air Force will be maintaining aircraft development at an accelerated pace. Flights will be made originally much in the manner of the X-15. A B-52 mother plane will carry the spacecraft to high altitude, and then drop the vehicle for unpowered, subsonic glide tests and landings. Then the speed will be increased to the transonic range—just below, at, and just above the speed of sound—to determine handling characteristics as the sonic shock waves build up about the spacecraft. Finally, the Dyna-Soar pilots will switch on rocket motors to enter the supersonic regions for accelerated handling-characteristics tests.

Astronauts will be trained for Dyna-Soar space flights in specially modified jet fighters. These will carry duplicate cockpit control systems for the student space pilot to practice maneuvers. The Air Force and NASA hope to join their training forces much more closely than at present, and perhaps have the Dyna-Soar pilots check out thoroughly in the X-15. In this manner they gain air-drop experience, rocket-firing experience, and the invaluable experience of actually racing out into near-vacuum conditions. The X-15 pilots will be using jet reaction controls and they will face all the problems and hazards

Dyna-Soar in orbit

of re-entry—high metal temperatures from friction, and gliding back to earth in a powerless, high-speed glider.

While in space, states the Air Force, the Dyna-Soar pilots "in the orbital regime" will carry out a series of experiments to determine "the tasks the manned vehicle can do in space."

Despite the military nature of the Dyna-Soar vehicle, there is an extensive and fully developed co-ordination program between the Air Force and NASA in the effort. Ira H. Abbott, Director of NASA's Advanced Research Programs, explains the role that NASA plays with the Air Force in the Dyna-Soar program:

" . . . the X-15 program is tied very intensively and carefully into the Dyna-Soar program in a general sense in that the research information which is being received from it as well as much of the practical operating experience has already had a considerable effect on the general thinking of the Dyna-Soar project. Of course, within NASA the people who are working on both projects are very closely associated and in many cases are the same people.

"As one illustration of this, at the time the Dyna-Soar was first started, there was a great deal of uncertainty as to the landing characteristics that would have to be built into it in order to permit landing on a runway. At that time, of course, we did not have the experience with the X-15 which lands very fast and with a very high rate of descent. Actually it has turned out during the operation of the X-15 that no undue difficulty has been encountered. This has lent a great deal more confidence to the Dyna-Soar design and has even permitted the design to back off a little from what was previously considered to be necessary for it. So in matters like this, there is a great deal of correlation and impact upon the new project."

Boss-Wedge

Project Mercury is the builder of a foundation of knowledge and experience—the starting point from which we are able to push into the more advanced programs of Gemini and Apollo. In similar fashion, the first one-man Dyna-Soar spacecraft will establish the foundation of experience and knowledge for future aerospace vehicles to follow. The latter machines will not be re-search craft as is the Dyna-Soar. Instead, they will be efficient, powerful craft capable of carrying out a wide variety of military reconnaissance, survey, interception, study, and, if necessary, even attack missions as combat spacecraft.

Dyna-Soar landing in California desert

For several years the Air Force has carried out an extensive study of the possibilities and uses to which it may one day need to put military space vehicles. The project is known as "BOSS-WEDGE." "BOSS" is derived from Bomb Orbital Strategic System; "WEDGE" comes from Weapon Development Glide Entry.

Under the direction of the Boeing Company (which has prime contract responsibility to develop the Dyna-Soar), scientists and engineers have been investigating many different possibilities, concepts, and proposals for space bomber vehicles. In this study effort, the Dyna-Soar figures strongly as the baseline guide from which to project future capabilities.

The weapon studies included projects for Dyna-Soar II, Dyna-Soar III, and Dyna-Mows. The more advanced vehicle, Dyna-Mows, is actually a highly developed Dyna-Soar III, to be used as a Manned Orbital Weapon System.

The Air Force found it necessary to ask itself a question that would determine much of its future research efforts. What are the means, the manner, and the different avenues along which there may be a need to employ the manned space weapon system? The Air Force makes no attempt to hide its strong dislike for the approach taken by the Department of Defense toward military weapon systems. The DOD attitude is that unless a specific mission can beyond all question be demonstrated *now* for a space weapon system, it will not authorize the funding necessary to carry out such research.

The weakness of this blindfolded approach is suggested when we recall that our top military leaders in 1907—when the Army bought its first airplane—said that the airplane would *never* be good for anything other than aerial observation over the trenches. The attitude was that it could fly faster than a horse could run, but that little else could be said for its merits or its future.

The Air Force is gravely concerned that this same attitude—or its parallel today—may cost us dearly in the future. If it turns out that military space systems hold a tremendous potential and use for a nation, we may be in the position of having the

Russians demonstrate those facts to *us*, just as in 1945 we demonstrated the versatility of fleets of B-29s to the Japanese.

In the interim—restricted to a budget-slashed Dyna-Soar program—the Air Force has gone ahead with its extensive studies in order to establish a hard and solid foundation of the potentiali ties in military space systems. If ever the need is demonstrated, we will have precious little time in which to move. It is not at all difficult to convert a military spacecraft into a scientific research vehicle, but the opposite, unfortunately, does not hold true at all.

The studies have included both unmanned and manned vehicles: weapons carriers operating in (1) an orbital regime no higher than 1,200 miles above the earth; and (2) weapons carriers that would orbit in space at altitudes greater than 12,000 miles.

Intensive efforts have been directed toward the program to develop manned weapon systems that would orbit the earth at 23,000 miles. At this height the orbital vehicle would drift within a restricted area over any point on earth, since at 23,000 miles the speed of the spaceship in orbit will match the speed of the earth's surface (as it rotates) directly beneath the ship. The true "fixed orbit" where the spaceship remains almost directly overhead in its orbit would have to be made along the equatorial zone.

Will we truly need military systems in space? It's impossible to draw any conclusions except, perhaps, just one:

There is no guarantee that in leaving his world behind him, man will also leave on earth the same causes and impulses that lead him to war.

XIII : *By Apollo to the Moon*

LAST YEAR, for the first time since the Russians led the way into orbit about our world, the United States committed itself to a massive, no-holds-barred effort in space. And no mere satellite program, this.

This time we were shooting—literally—for the moon. This time we were throwing behind that effort not only the resources of the nation, but the full weight of the Executive Office as well.

President Kennedy spoke to the United States:

"Now it is time to act, to take longer strides—time for a great new American enterprise—time for this nation to take a clearly leading role in space achievement. . . . I believe that the Nation should commit itself to achieving that goal, before the decade is out, of landing a man on the moon and returning him safely to earth."

For the first time, finally—it had happened. The President had spoken *for* a major space effort, had thrown the weight of his office and his prestige behind the lunar-landing program of the United States.

Project Apollo, which had moved slowly since its inception in 1959, suddenly blossomed overnight. It had purpose, meaning, vigor, drive, urgency—everything it needed. There has always been an underlying theme in the American space effort. Our science and our scientists have never been wanting in their knowledge or their capabilities. Politically, however, their nation had crippled their efforts, denied them funds, refused them authority to act. More by default, than by anything else—and this is not deprecation of our adversaries' own vast strides—we plunged far behind the Russians who pushed out into the cosmos with a national urgency and purpose that was remarkable.

Who would be first to reach the moon? Who would gain that enormous prestige internationally that pays such great dividends in relations between nations of the world? The Russians are trying hard, *very* hard. Behind them they have a list of stunning achievements. The first satellite into orbit about the earth . . . the first living creature ever to go into space . . . the first rocket to pass close by the moon, to enter into solar orbit . . . the first rocket *on* the moon . . . the first laboratory to take pictures of the other side of the moon . . . the first animals in space brought safely back to earth . . . the first probe to another planet . . . the first man in orbit . . . the first man to make a flight of more than one full day and night in space . . .

There are several "great prizes" left in terms of international prestige—as urgently sought by us as by the USSR. There will be the first multi-man mission in space, the first "soft" landing on the moon with major instruments, the first flight of men around the moon. Who will make these flights? As regards manned flights, we are willing to concede that most likely the Soviets will do so.

Who will be first to land on the moon? Some Americans—including NASA Administrator James E. Webb—believe that we will have Americans walking on the surface of the moon before the Russians can do so. Most fervently I hope Mr. Webb turns out to be an accurate prophet in this respect. Most realistically, I believe he is going to be wrong. No matter how fast we run now, it always takes some time to catch up, and I do not believe for an instant that the Russians are so naïve as to throw away a commanding lead for some time to come in rocket booster power. By 1970? Well, by then booster power won't matter much any more. Both countries will have rockets so enormous that payloads will be measured in hundreds of thousands of pounds, and the international weighing of payloads that is so vital today will by then become meaningless.

President Kennedy has made it clear that the program to reach the moon will be nothing less than overwhelmingly complex and costly: "No single space project . . . will be more impressive to mankind," he said. "None will be so difficult or expensive to accomplish. . . . While we cannot guarantee that we shall one day be first, we can guarantee that any failure to make this effort will make us last. . . . We go into space because whatever mankind must undertake, free man must fully share."

Project Apollo is an undertaking that will require a decade from its start (as a design project study in 1959) to its major realized goal—men safely on the moon, and safely returned to the surface of the earth. It will cost at least *twenty billion* dollars —and likely it will return many times that amount in scientific knowledge, technological capabilities, and our position in the world.

"This venture will require technological advancements far in excess of those needed for Project Mercury or Project Gemini," explains D. Brainerd Holmes, the NASA Director of Manned Space Flight. "It will require the development of an advanced spacecraft that can withstand the high loads of launching,

Solid-booster flight test of Apollo spacecraft

Nova vehicle at launch

that can be guided and steered toward the moon, that can land gently on the moon, and then be launched from the moon and guided back toward the safe re-entry and recovery on earth. It will require the development of several launch vehicles, the largest of which will be more than 30 times as powerful as the Atlas booster, and of propulsion systems for the lunar landing and takeoff.

"The Apollo objective is to accomplish a manned lunar landing and return at the earliest practicable date. As a corollary objective, a manned orbiting laboratory for conducting a variety of scientific and technological experiments will be developed."

Robert R. Gilruth, who has guided in brilliant fashion the Mercury program, explains the Apollo craft in more detail:

"It is felt that a scheme of successive tests and missions, each of increased difficulty or complexity, is the best means of developing spacecraft for manned flight. This is the traditional method employed in prototype testing of aircraft and is also the method used in the Mercury project. This method is ideally suited to the Apollo spacecraft since it allows for manned flight on early missions of reduced hazard and is in keeping with the development of the nation's launch vehicle capability. The Saturn C-1 will be suitable for earth-orbital missions. An Advanced Saturn will carry the spacecraft to escape velocity and will be suitable for circumlunar and lunar-orbital flights. The lunar-landing mission may be made with some type of rendezvous scheme using Saturn launch vehicles or by the direct approach with a large launch vehicle.

Exact size mockup of the Apollo spaceship's Command Module, inspected by North American Aviation's engineers Charles Feltz and Robert Templeton.

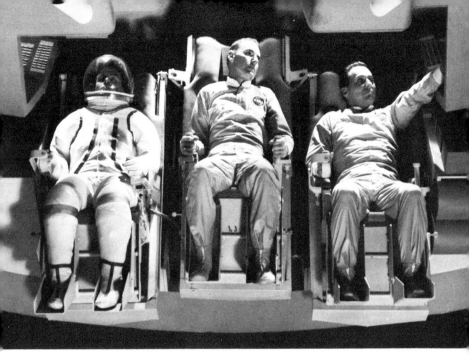

Cutaway view of mockup of Apollo Command Module, showing crew positions for flight operations.

"The Apollo spacecraft will be primarily designed for its lunar mission. Nevertheless, it will be suited for other missions. It will be capable of rendezvous and, therefore, should work well in support of orbital space stations and laboratories. It will be designed to provide adequate accommodations for a 14-day-duration mission with the three-man crew. With only minor modifications, it should be able to carry double that number of men on flights of short duration.

". . . It is intended to man the Apollo spacecraft on the earliest possible flight. Men will go aboard during the first orbit missions of the complete spacecraft. They will then fly missions of increasing difficulty and will thereby greatly enhance the development program. In order to achieve maximum benefit from the integration of man into the space vehicle and to assure maximum possibility of mission success, it is imperative that the flight crews be men experienced in the operation and testing of high-performance aircraft. Although man may not be in

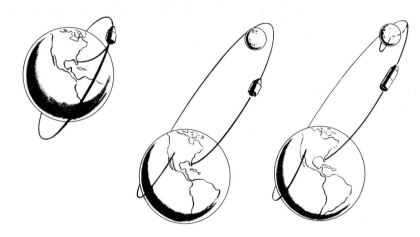

Apollo in earth orbit   *Circumlunar orbit*   *Apollo landing on moon*

the primary launch-vehicle guidance loop during launch, backup control or abort decisions will be required that will demand rapid response times similar to those encountered in modern aircraft. Systems management, navigation, re-entry, and landing techniques will be similar, in many respects, to those encountered in aircraft practice. Since the investment involved in each advanced manned space mission will be on an order of magnitude greater than the cost of today's aircraft or space missions, it is clear that the most experienced and capable flight crews must be selected.

"The lunar flight crew, as currently planned, will consist of three men: spacecraft commander/pilot; navigator/copilot; and systems manager. The spacecraft commander and navigator will be thoroughly cross-trained in the propulsion and attitude control of the spacecraft, navigation, on-board computer calculations, communications, and over-all systems operation. The detailed duties for the systems manager will become defined as the system design progresses. He will be somewhat cross-trained in the pilots' positions and will be capable of performing the earth re-entry and landing maneuver. The primary responsibility of the systems manager will be the management of the various propulsion systems, especially during the lunar landing and lunar takeoff. Dependent upon use of the rendezvous techniques for the lunar mission, the third crewman may also be involved in vehicle checkout subsequent to the docking operation.

"The Apollo development program is not without problems. In the area of human factors there are two potential problems. These are the effects of long periods of weightlessness and the intensity and nature of radiation emanating from solar disturbances. Physiological problems resulting from weightlessness cannot be discounted until we have indeed exposed human subjects to a true weightless environment for a duration equal to the mission. While recent analysis of solar radiation provides encouraging results, we cannot provide adequate protection against the maximum solar flares nor are we certain of a suitable technique for predicting such flares. . . ."

And that is the best accounting the author has ever seen of just what Apollo means—in terms of solving the great problems that face its success. It is a combination of spacecraft technology, of *planetary* guidance and control, human factors stretched to a degree far beyond anything we have attained, propulsion systems with reliability to make engineers turn gray . . . This, then, is Apollo!

The Spaceship

Unlike the previous Mercury and Gemini spacecraft, Apollo is a grouping of what NASA calls *modules*. The actual part of the Apollo system in which the astronauts will operate is the Command Module. Gilruth describes this section as "in many respects, the Command Module will be a large version of the Mercury. . . . the crew will be supported during launch in approximately the same manner and position as used in Mercury."

The Command Module has a squatter shape than the Mercury or Gemini capsules. Across the base Apollo is 13 feet wide, and it reaches at the top of its sharply converging cone-shape a height of 12 feet. Because it is more "squat" than Mercury, unlike both Mercury and Gemini, Apollo will be able to exert a modest amount of aerodynamic lift during re-entry. It will streak back into the atmosphere with a speed of nearly 25,000 miles per

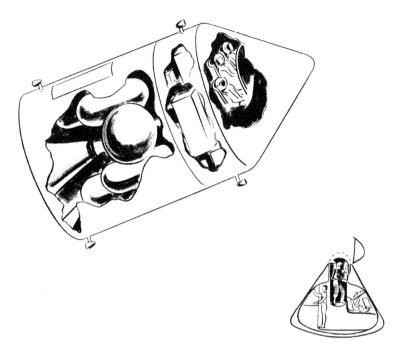

Apollo in circumlunar configuration   Schematic view of Apollo Command
Module

hours—thus the "squat" shape to avoid excessive heating on the
afterbody of the capsule at "the trimmed angle of attack." This
means that the capsule will not re-enter with its longitudinal
axis (a line drawn directly through the center of the capsule,
from top to bottom) directly along the line of flight. Instead, the
capsule will be tilted very slightly upward in its attitude.

Inside the capsule—the Command Module—the three men will
each have a separate contour couch, aligned in a row. This configuration is for launch and re-entry. During the long orbit to
the moon, or during earth orbit, the center couch swings away
and is moved against the interior spaceship wall, creating a working space for the crew. The module will contain display panels,
navigation equipment, communications systems, and the many
different controls and instruments necessary for in-space operations.

There are separate areas for preparing meals (including

cooking), for sleeping, and for sanitary functions. Special equipment particularly vital to the mission for repairs such as minor equipment adjustments, calibrations, and cross-checking will be kept in the Command Module.

During launch, a tower and escape rocket will be standard equipment for the Apollo spacecraft. This rocket will have a firing thrust of 200,000 pounds and must burn at maximum thrust for at least two seconds. Another requirement is that the escape rocket must achieve 90 per cent of maximum thrust within a few thousandths of a second after the firing switch is thrown. As in Mercury, the escape tower and rocket will be jettisoned during the ascent of the booster vehicle.

The Apollo Command Module seats can be tilted to different positions for the astronauts—sitting, reclining, launch, and others. This mockup cut-away view shows the center contour couch moved against the far bulkhead in its sleeping position, leaving a working space in the exact center of the spaceship. The thick tube in top center is the airlock for leaving the spaceship in vacuum.

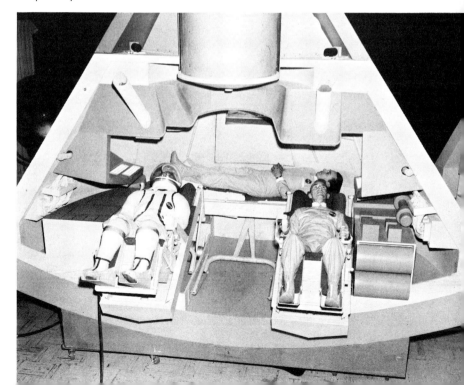

The other two elements of what is described as the "complete Apollo spaceship" are the Service Module and the Lunar Landing Module. As a single unit, standing vertically, the Apollo Command Module is the highest, the Service Module is in the center, and the Lunar Landing Module forms the base.

Completely assembled, the Apollo spaceship weighs 150,000 pounds and stands as high as a five-story building!

The Service Module contains those components of the spaceship that are not needed directly within the Command Module —the pressurized compartment that makes up the top of the squat-shaped Apollo. This is an ingenious solution to the problems of weight and size for re-entry, as well as efficiency in space. Since the living quarters demand the highest perfection of equipment—*and* constant pressurization and maintenance of living standards—it seems unnecessary to enlarge the living area and at the same time increase enormously the complexity and operation of this part of the spacecraft. It would be something like furnishing the cargo compartment of an airliner with all the equipment and services of the passenger cabin.

At the same time, restricting the re-entry part of the spaceship to the Command Module immediately strips the re-entry and recovery process of enormous problems. The greater the size and weight of the re-entry vehicle at 25,000 miles per hour, the greater the hazards and the chances for failure. Recovery becomes a major problem as well. It is far easier and less costly in the long run to dispose effectively of this Service Module equipment by incineration than to attempt its successful re-entry and recovery.

Inside the Service Module are contained some of the breathing oxygen, the electrical power supplies, the propulsion used for guidance corrections in trips between moon and earth, propulsion for emergency abort situations, and for lunar takeoff.

Third and final module is the Lunar Landing Module—a powerful propulsion stage that decelerates the spaceship during approach and descent to the moon, and performs the actual landing on the moon.

One of the truly great advantages of the modular approach to space flight—and it is not yet recognized for the superb method

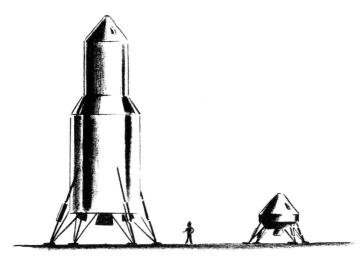

Comparison of Apollo vs. Lunar Ferry

that it represents—is that along with the development cycle of the equipment, the United States gains all the advantages of a multiple system of spacecraft that adapt easily and well to a variety of missions in space.

During the early space flights, the astronauts will be able not only to gain proficiency in their equipment handling, as well as invaluable orbital flight experience, but they can—and will—test many intricate spacecraft subsystems. Such tests before the lunar missions are ready for dispatch allow the equipment to be checked out thoroughly—to be modified, replaced, accepted, or discarded altogether. Malfunctions in equipment can be corrected by the crews who will spend two weeks in orbit, simulating exactly the time for the lunar mission. Such corrections, repairs, and findings would be impossible to effect on the actual lunar flight and—were they not discovered before committing the moon mission—might even cause that mission to fail.

Another simultaneous program will be the carrying out of many extensive scientific experiments. Apollo is large enough to function as an orbiting, manned laboratory—and the boosters to enable Apollo's success are powerful enough to orbit space stations weighing more than 200 tons with a single firing!

"When used with an orbiting laboratory module," explains Brainerd Holmes, "the spacecraft in earth-orbit will provide a testbed for technological development and for scientific observations.

"In this connection, it will be possible to obtain aerospace medical data on animals—data of a kind that cannot be obtained on men. Animals can be instrumented with devices that are not acceptable for men, devices such as deep brain probes and implanted blood-flow sensors. Such tests should provide detailed knowledge concerning the effects of space flight. Experiments could be performed over very long periods of time if the laboratory is resupplied, using rendezvous techniques.

"The Command Module itself will be one of the most complex manned-flight devices ever designed and built. It will contain many systems required to perform the mission, including the environmental-control system needed to provide the proper atmosphere for the duration of the flight; a communication system to allow the men to be in contact with the control center on earth; a guidance and control system, together with its associated computing devices and pilot displays, to allow for the proper execution of the mission; a landing system to provide for a touchdown at a fixed point on earth. Each of these systems will entail a major development effort. Light weight, high performance, and high reliability will be basic requirements."

One single indication of the magnitude of the problems involved: during re-entry at 25,000 miles per hour the heating rates of Apollo will be *ten times higher* than those of Mercury!

The industrial team that will develop Apollo is the true giant of the space industry in America—North American Aviation, Inc., whose Space and Information Systems Division is already hard at work with more than a thousand top engineers and scientists on Apollo. North American's Rocketdyne Division builds the motors for the Redstone, Thor, Jupiter, Atlas, Saturn C-1, Saturn C-5, Nova, and other vehicles—and it might well be said that America has reached out into space by virtue of the propulsion systems of Rocketdyne.

In its initial phase the Apollo contract—for the Command and Service Modules—runs to almost a half-billion dollars. But this is only the *initial* phase of the contract. It will far exceed this figure by the time the moon is reached.

Apollo will be built at Downey, California, where North American is assembling what may well turn out to be the most capable space-design team in the entire world. The Apollo team will exist within the North American framework, but it will be able to make its own hard-and-fast decisions as its sees fit to bring the Apollo project along smoothly and quickly. North American's plan is not to allow the parent company to interfere with Apollo, but to stand by to assist to the maximum with whatever the Apollo team needs for this vital effort.

One hundred crack scientists and engineers have been working for a long time on Apollo, and the technical staff is being added to mainly from within the corporation family. The hard core of the team is made up of the team which engineered and built the sensationally successful X-15—and more members of the X-15 family are coming into Apollo. The corporation considers the X-15 team as a "real gung-ho outfit." Harrison A. Storms, SISD's president, explains that the team has "been through this once. They know what to look for and are well seasoned." Storms emphasizes that his close-knit group have worked together for more than a decade, and that many of them have been with North American for more than 20 years.

Spaceship components are already undergoing extensive testing, and experimental spacecraft will be available for testing before the end of 1962. The first complete spacecraft for full-scale flight testing will be delivered to NASA in 1964, according to present scheduling, and if things continue to progress with the giant boosters now under accelerated flight development, the unmanned Apollo may be in earth orbit before 1965.

If—and it is still a very big *if*—the entire mass program moves along its most optimistic schedules, the United States may be ready for its first manned landing on the moon sometime in 1967.

Boosters and Scheduling

The success of Apollo depends upon many factors. First, there is the *simultaneous* development of the spacecraft, the giant boosters, and perfection of the rendezvous techniques in space.

The immediate key to this program is still Project Mercury,

In a "preview" of a flight scheduled for 1964–65, the Saturn C-1 booster thunders up from Cape Canaveral. When used as a two-stage booster for ten-ton Apollo spaceship, C-1 booster will develop 1,500,000 pounds thrust in the first stage and will weigh 1,100,000 pounds at launch.

which must progress through several three-orbit flights, the seven-orbit flight (possibly to be assigned in 1962), and finally the mission of 18 orbits with one man. Mercury remains, however, essentially what it always has been—a means of obtaining baseline data on which to build the succeeding effort, Project Gemini.

How fast will Gemini move? No hard-and-fast answer is possible to this question. The original plans for Gemini *already are slipping* badly enough to create some unhappiness within NASA.

The critical problem here is not the spacecraft or even the time needed to "get the booster man-rated" from its status as a missile. It takes a long time to build the launch facilities at Canaveral for these programs. Early in 1962 NASA estimated that modification of Pad 19 on Canaveral to accommodate the Titan II booster with the Gemini spacecraft would take some 20 months, making possible launchings sometime late in 1963. But this construction program hasn't gone as rapidly as we'd hoped, and that schedule is slipping—pushing back the entire effort.

It's difficult to make forecasts in an area so obviously diverse as this one—but by the summer of 1962 the chances for a first manned Gemini flight in 1963 are not particularly appealing. The following year—the spring of 1964—seems to be more realistic.

There's another possible catch—the development and acceptance of the Titan II *missile*. The first Titan II lifted from Cape Canaveral on March 16, 1962, in a perfect test—the missile arced 5,000 miles down the Atlantic Missile Range. The Air Force plans to fire at least 12 of the powerful missiles during a test program that is anticipated to last at the very minimum for 12 months, and more likely for 18 months. This could well mean that not until the fall of 1963 would the missile be out of its military development program, which is a long way from being man-rated for Gemini. Any failures in the military development series (Titan I tests required 34 months and the firing of 47 missiles from Canaveral) could throw the entire time schedule for Gemini

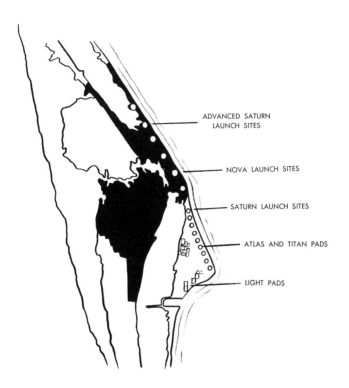

Cape Canaveral launch complexes

into a cocked hat, and snarl up the full rendezvous program. The Air Force is using Pads 16 and 15 on the Cape for the Titan II development series shots. Failures of a rocket affect a program in different ways. It's one thing to have the rocket explode in the air, for example, but quite something else to experience that explosion on the actual launching platform. Damage can run into the millions of dollars and take many months to repair.

Bootstraps for Apollo

Both Projects Mercury and Gemini have involved only one rocket booster in each program for sending the manned spacecraft into orbit. With Mercury we have had the Atlas-D vehicle; with Gemini, the Titan II (and, especially, the Titan III for Dyna-Soar). But behind the manned orbital flights of Mercury have been other rockets. One was a thick cluster of solid-propellant rockets into a single booster vehicle called *Little Joe*. These rockets were fired from the NASA station at Wallops Island, Virginia, in flight tests of the unmanned Mercury capsule.

After the *Little Joe* shots, NASA moved to the Redstone booster to make a series of unmanned flights. Then a chimpanzee was fired along a suborbital arc, and, finally, we had the flights of Shepard and Grissom.

The sequence was repeated with the Atlas (including one unmanned firing called *Big Joe*). An unmanned capsule went into orbit, then a capsule with the chimpanzee Enos, and, finally, the manned *Friendship 7* spacecraft with Glenn.

Long before Apollo is ready for its flight tests as a full vehicle, many of the large spaceships will be airborne. North American Aviation will be making extensive flight tests with a new solid-propellant booster called *Little Joe II*, an assembly of massive solid-propellant rockets to hurl the heavy Apollo high above the earth. There will be tests to fire the 200,000-pound escape rocket, to fire tower jettison rockets, posigrades, retros, and many other propulsion systems.

The first orbital flights of the unmanned spacecraft will be made with the giant Saturn C-1 booster, which in its first two test flights scored perfect successes. Saturn C-1 consists of eight H.1 engines combined in a single big cluster to produce approximately 1,500,000 pounds thrust as an operational vehicle. (The first four test flights were flown with the engines rated at 165,000 pounds thrust each for a total of approximately 1,300,000 pounds thrust total for the first stage.)

One of the strange aspects of Saturn C-1 is that originally this was a military booster for the Dyna-Soar program, developed under the auspices of the Advanced Research Projects Agency (ARPA). After the formation in 1958 of NASA, the booster was assigned to that space agency for a variety of programs—including Apollo.

Saturn C-1 as a boost-vehicle for the Apollo manned program consists of two stages. The first stage is S-I and the second stage is S-IV (a third stage, the S-V, is used for unmanned missions of instrument packages to the moon and other planets).

There are ten test flights planned to develop the Saturn C-1 and bring it to "man-rated" status. In the first four flight tests, only the S-I first-stage booster is alive; the two upper stages are dummies carrying water ballast.

In the fifth flight, scheduled for 1963, the two booster stages will be live, and they will attempt to send an Apollo mockup on a major vehicle test flight. As the flights continue, the Apollo in different unmanned configurations will be fired into orbit.

The Saturn C-1 vehicle as an Apollo booster, in its final configuration, will weigh 1,100,000 pounds—and will stand more than 170 feet tall!

Stage I will have four large aerodynamic fins added to the booster to give C-1 a capability for broadly varied missions in the future. The eight H.1 engines are arranged in two groups: the four inboard engines are rigidly secured to the booster framework and are canted at a three-degree angle to the centerline of the booster; the outboard engines are canted at an angle of six degrees as well as being mounted on gimbals that permit them to be turned through angles of up to 7.5 degrees to provide vehicle directional control during the ascent.

The engines will burn with a liftoff thrust of 1,500,000 pounds, consuming kerosene and liquid oxygen. Shutdown of the engines comes at 120 seconds after the firing begins. If motor failure occurs during flight, the fuel assigned to that one motor is automatically shunted to the other motors, thus providing Saturn C-1 with an "engine-out" flight capability. The remaining engines will consume all available fuel, and the 120-second burning time will be increased. There is only a minor loss in over-all booster performance.

Stage II—the S-IV—is a high-energy vehicle. The size of the C-1 system can be appreciated when we see that this second stage has six A.3 engines, each of 15,000 pounds thrust (90,000 pounds thrust normal rating; S-IV also has engine-out capability). The S-IV—remember that this is the *upper stage*—is 18 feet in diameter and 40 feet in length! S-IV burns a combination of liquid oxygen/liquid hydrogen—almost half again as powerful as a similar stage of the same size and weight burning kerosene and liquid oxygen.

Operational configuration of Saturn C-1 (note fins) during launching of Apollo spaceship into earth orbit. First stage has burned out; second stage with 90,000 pounds thrust has just ignited and is beginning powered flight to orbital speed of 17,100 miles per hour.

The development of the C-1 vehicle in its early stages has been one of the wonders of the space age. The first two flights were as perfect as they could possibly be. The second vehicle (called SA-2; each vehicle will be numbered in the SA series, starting with SA-1, etc.) went through its 12-hour countdown without a single technical interruption.

The two sets of engines—inboard and outboard—are cut off (shut down) in a staggered arrangement; the inboards cut off first and the outboards cut off some six seconds later. This is done to prevent "unacceptable oscillations" which might occur if all engines were shut down simultaneously. Also, in this fashion, it's possible to attain a more complete consumption of available fuel.

Saturn C-1 will be used in the manned Apollo flights to send payloads of 20,000 pounds into a low orbit about the earth. With the Service Module attached to the Command Module, Apollo with its three-man crew can be boosted into orbit with a payload of ten tons, to remain in space for a period of 14 days—a necessary prelude to the flights around the moon and then, finally, on to the moon itself.

We are familiar with the great size of the gantry work tower to support the Atlas-boosted Mercury missions. But even this impressive structure is a toy compared to the facilities of Saturn Launch Complex 34 on Canaveral, a launch complex covering 45 acres on the north end of the Cape. The workstand for Saturn C-1 is 310 feet high—and weighs over 2,800 tons! Despite this ponderous size, the workstand is movable.

The Launch Control Center (a radical new type of blockhouse and flight-control facility) has walls 12 feet thick. The single door to the Center is of solid steel, two feet thick and weighing 46,000 pounds.

Advanced Saturn

Recently the National Aeronautics and Space Administration acquired 73,000 acres of land to the north and west of Cape Canaveral. Some people call this area "moonland"; they are not as facetious as it might seem, for this is the area from which will ascend the great rockets bound for the moon.

Saturn C-1 is an enormous advance in size, weight, and power over the most powerful rocket flown in the United States to date, the Titan II (full-staging). Titan II generates 430,000 pounds thrust for its first stage and 100,000 pounds thrust for its second stage. By comparison, C-1 develops 1,500,000 pounds for Stage I and 90,000 pounds thrust for Stage II. The latter, as pointed out, is actually more powerful than the Titan II upper stage; the C-1 upper stage has engine-out capability and it burns the high-energy fuel of liquid oxygen/liquid hydrogen. Pound-for-pound, it delivers more power than the Titan upper stage. Saturn C-1 in launch configuration weighs 550 tons.

It is difficult to realize, then, that the enormous increase represented in the C-1 over previous vehicles is being greatly exceeded with new boosters—the Saturn C-5 and the Nova.

Saturn C-1's first stage has eight engines, clustered together to produce 1,500,000 pounds thrust.

Rocketdyne F.1 liquid-propellant motor under test in static stand. This single motor has more power than the entire Saturn space booster to send Apollo into earth orbit! The motor is 14 feet wide, 20 feet high!

Saturn C-5 in its first stage (S-IB) has five engines—known as the F.1. *Each* combustion chamber of the C-5 vehicle—each F.1 engine—stands 20 feet high and measures 14 feet across the nozzle exit.

Each *one* of these F.1 engines produces 1,500,000 pounds thrust. Thus, Saturn C-5 generates 7,500,000 pounds thrust at launch!

The Saturn C-5 fuel tanks are 33 feet in diameter—and the first stage alone stands 140 feet high. Like the "small C-1" vehicle, this Advanced Saturn has engine-out capability.

Even Stage II is enormous. It is 33 feet in diameter and 70 feet high. It burns high-energy fuels through five J.2 engines, each of which delivers 200,000 pounds thrust for a second-stage power rating of 1,000,000 pounds.

This giant booster with only these two stages can place—in a single firing—into a low earth orbit a payload of more than 200,000 pounds—more than 100 tons in a single launching.

When used as the booster vehicle for a circumlunar flight—takeoff from the earth and directly out into space at 25,000 miles per hour—a third stage is to be added to the C-5. This third stage is 18 feet in diameter and 60 feet in length. Its single J.2 engine

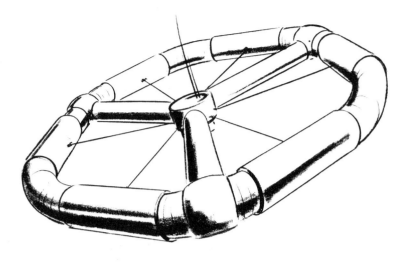

Fifteen-man ring-type orbital station

develops 200,000 pounds thrust, burning high-energy fuels.

The three-stage Saturn C-5, with the Apollo payload (Command Service Modules, escape tower, and escape rocket) stands more than 300 feet high.

Ready on the launching pad for the flight of the Apollo around the moon and back to earth, Saturn C-5 weighs more than *three thousand tons.*

Adjectives become meaningless after describing the awesome size, weight, power, and capabilities of the Saturn C-5 launch-vehicle system. Today, when we measure every pound we put into orbit, it seems impossible that within five years we hope to be sending single-shot payloads of 200,000 pounds into orbit about the earth.

A flight to the moon—including landing the 75-ton Apollo spaceship with three complete modules—can be accomplished by using the Saturn C-5 with the rendezvous technique. Two Saturn C-5 boosters in the two-stage configuration are used, each to orbit a payload of 100 tons. One payload is made up of a fuel-tank-and-engines system; the other is the three-module Apollo.

The two payloads rendezvous in orbit. The crew goes through rendezvous and docking. Then the fuel-tank-and-engines pay-

C-5 BOOSTER

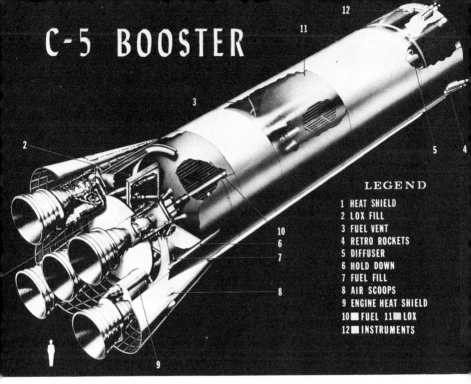

LEGEND

1 HEAT SHIELD
2 LOX FILL
3 FUEL VENT
4 RETRO ROCKETS
5 DIFFUSER
6 HOLD DOWN
7 FUEL FILL
8 AIR SCOOPS
9 ENGINE HEAT SHIELD
10 ■ FUEL 11 ■ LOX
12 ■ INSTRUMENTS

This is the Saturn C-5 booster with five F.1 motors. The first stage of Saturn C-5 shown here develops 7,500,000 pounds thrust at launch! Note the size of the man in comparison with the huge C-5 vehicle. At launch configuration with the Apollo spaceship, Saturn C-5 will weigh 3,000 tons. With a second stage of five J.2 motors totaling 1,000,000 pounds thrust, Saturn C-5 can place 200,000 pounds of payload into orbit with a single firing.

load is used to boost the Apollo spaceship from orbital speed to earth escape velocity of 25,000 miles per hour. The empty fuel tanks are jettisoned—and the mission to land on the moon has begun.

But what if the rendezvous method *doesn't* work? What happens if the experiments in orbit about the earth show that rendezvous and docking is a dangerous procedure—too dangerous for us to count on for the vital moon program?

NASA is considering that possibility as well as all others. In the event that this does come to pass—however unlikely it may be—the answer then is . . .

Surveyor robot spaceship descending to moon

Nova

One engineer calls the Nova booster "a volcano packaged neatly into the biggest tin can you ever saw." Perhaps this description isn't properly technical, but it's as apt as I've ever 'heard in respect to this gargantua of the space age.

Whether or not rendezvous works, Nova is an active project. It will be able to send the 150,000-pound Apollo spaceship from the earth's surface directly to the moon, and no stops or rendezvous on the way. As much as Saturn C-1 dwarfs Titan II—and Saturn C-5 dwarfs Saturn C-1—so Nova dwarfs even the mammoth C-5.

For its first stage, Nova uses eight of the powerful F.1 engines. This means a first-stage thrust at liftoff of *twelve million pounds.* The first stage of Nova—*each* engine is as powerful as the *entire* Saturn C-1 booster—is 45 feet in *diameter.*

Stage II represents a behemoth in itself. It is powered with four Aerojet M.1 engines burning the high-energy liquid oxygen/liquid hydrogen fuel. *Each* engine with this high-energy fuel delivers 1,200,000 pounds thrust, for a second-stage combined total (Stage II also has engine-out capability) of 4,800,000 pounds thrust. The diameter is 45 feet.

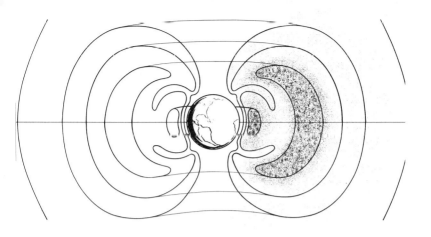

Van Allen radiation belts about the earth

Stage III will be the same booster as that used atop the Saturn C-5 for direct circumlunar flights—the one J.2 engine of 200,000 pounds thrust.

Figures speak for themselves. On the launch pad, with the 75-ton Apollo as the payload, the Nova launch vehicle will stand nearly 400 feet high.

The launch weight is 10,000,000 pounds.

Nova will send into an earth orbit 300 miles high—in a single firing—a payload of at least *two hundred tons.*

Moon Missions

The first flights of Apollo to the moon will be strictly "sightseeing trips." The heavy spacecraft will leave the vicinity of the earth with a speed just below 25,000 miles per hour, moving along an orbit calculated with great precision. The idea of the flight is to bring the Apollo close by the moon's surface, around the far side of the moon in a giant swing, and then back toward the earth. "In the circumlunar flight the crew will, for the first time, perform the complicated guidance and navigation task of steering the craft toward the moon," explains Brainerd Holmes. They will steer "in an orbit around the moon, and on its flight back toward the earth. While in the vicinity of the moon, the crew

Apollo three-module spaceship on the moon—standing five stories tall. Three-module Apollo weighs 150,000 pounds as it leaves orbit of earth. The space-ship swings once around the moon (upper left), comes entirely around the airless world to begin its rocket-braking approach (right center) to land. The main body of the spaceship is used as a launch platform for upper two modules, and remains permanently on the moon. (Painting by Fred L. Wolff)

NASA *concept for one-man spaceship to descend to moon from lunar-orbiting Apollo spacecraft.*

will be able to personally survey the landing site that it will later use in a manned lunar landing mission. . . ."

But if the mission to the moon must be precise, then the return to the earth must be even more precise. For the three men in Apollo must return in a trajectory calculated to the ultimate.

Apollo must enter the upper edges of the earth's atmosphere within narrow limits—a corridor of re-entry no more than 40 miles wide. Forty miles may seem to be a rather large width for the flight of a vehicle, but not when that spacecraft is moving so fast that it can cross the 40-mile corridor *in less than six seconds.*

Further, the starting point for the entry corridor begins 250,000 miles away; the corrections made along the return must be calculated with the utmost care, and then must be made with virtually no margin of error. NASA scientists explain the accuracy required for this maneuver is akin to hitting dead-center, across an entire football field, a target no larger than a nickel.

For the circumlunar missions the Service Module will contain a complicated propulsion system into which reliability has been built at enormous cost. An emergency situation must be considered as possible at any point along the round trip of more than 500,000 miles.

The circumlunar mission will last, normally, about five days—120 hours of weightless flight. If an emergency occurs, states Holmes, "then the abort propulsion system can be used to return the craft to earth in a much shorter period of time."

To land on the moon, we have the complete Apollo spaceship that includes the Command Service, and Lunar Landing Modules. The Apollo will approach the moon along an orbit that carries the spaceship close to the lunar surface—grazing the surface is an apt description—and then around the far side of the moon. The propulsion system is fired to slow down the heavy spaceship so that it actually falls into an orbit about the moon.

If the ship were to approach the surface directly—such as an impact shot—the danger of failure is increased. Suppose, during this maneuver, the propulsion system failed to operate. The result would be fatal—the ship would continue on its collision course directly into the lunar surface. But if there is a failure in the "grazing maneuver"—why, the ship simply swings around the moon and can be directed back to earth.

Normally, after it has decelerated and has ben "captured" by the moon's gravity, the Apollo swings around the small world at a relatively close distance. Then, with all systems checked out, the propulsion system fires. The Apollo decelerates more and more as it approaches the lunar surface at an angle. Close to the moon, the spacecraft "pitches over" and descends vertically. As it reaches the surface its speed must be just about zero—almost like that of a helicopter touching down gently on the earth.

But without any air on the moon, everything in the landing maneuver is an infinitely fine, constantly adjusted manipulation of rocket energy.

Because the actual landing area may be rough or even unknown in terms of detail to us, the propulsion module of Apollo has a special landing gear to absorb the shock of the actual touchdown.

Man on the moon . . .
(Painting by Fred L.
Wolff)

Once on the moon, the crew immediately checks out all systems. They will land on that part of the surface facing the earth —a line-of-sight landing permitting communications to be carried on continuously (with a time-lag of messages of just less than two seconds, because of the distance). With Apollo thoroughly checked out, the astronauts will prepare for five days of exploration and experiments.

They will leave the Apollo Command Module through an airlock at the top of the spaceship, and climb a long ladder down to the moon surface—a climb of five stories down and five stories back up again. But even in the pressure suits that must be worn, their task will be eased, because on this airless, soundless, weatherless world the surface gravity is only one-sixth that of earth, and even the heaviest spacesuit will be no burden to its wearer.

Perhaps one of the more critical parts of the entire mission is leaving the moon. The countdown must be precise; the crew must take off at an exact moment that will bring them back to

Return to the earth . . . at 25,000 miles per hour. The Command Module of the Apollo spaceship as it plunges back into the earth's atmosphere with a speed of seven miles per second. It will be a critical, extremely dangerous return to the planet of origin . . . and the beginning of many future flights to the moon, and to other worlds.

earth at a *time and place* so that they can move into their re-entry corridor to land in the United States.

The entire "Cape Canaveral" of the moon will be the Apollo spaceship and its crew of three; support will come, of course, in terms of data computed by the electronic brains on the earth. The crew may have to make some minor repairs with whatever tools and parts can be carried to the moon.

When the countdown is ready, the motors in the Service Module will fire, burning storable propellants in pressurized tanks. The launching platform is the bottom part of Apollo itself —the Lunar Landing Module. The Service Module motors blast away in vacuum, pushing the squat spacecraft higher above the moon until the speed is just over 5,600 miles per hour. At this point the power can be cut, for the escape velocity of the moon is much less than that of earth. When the power is shut down and the Apollo is moving along its desired trajectory, then return to the earth is guaranteed.

On the way home, the men will carefully navigate their space-ship to be absolutely certain of coming down into the re-entry corridor at the precise moment and place as planned.

It will be a fiery, blazing return through the atmosphere—a plunge into the barrier reefs of friction at seven miles per second. Apollo will look like a great, flaming meteor crashing downward from space.

Then the speed will begin to slacken. Temperatures will halt their rise and begin to decrease rapidly. Apollo will drop into the lower, denser atmosphere. The drogue parachute will stabilize and further decelerate the moon spaceship.

Finally, doors will snap open, and the great batlike form of the parawing will push its way above the spaceship. It will fill out, flexing its surface, grasping with aerodynamic lift at the air. The men will guide their spacecraft through the air ocean toward that long, flat desert floor in California—their final maneuver accompanied by the quiet sound of the warm air of Earth whistling past the craft that has just completed a round-trip flight of 500,000 miles . . . to another world in space.

Apollo spacecraft with triple-parachute re-covery system

XIV : *Crash Program*

In July of 1962, the top officials of the National Aeronautics and Space Administration announced the results of a critical study which had been under way for more than a year. The United States would make a bold move toward slicing one to two years from its planned accelerated schedule to land the first Americans on the surface of the moon. If the new plan— which called for the daring technique of *rendezvous in a lunar orbit*—worked out as the officials believe it will, then the United States should have its best possible opportunity to actually beat the Russians to the manned lunar landing.

In the preceding chapter I pointed to the remarks of James E. Webb, the NASA Administrator, who stated that the United States would likely reach the lunar surface with our astronauts before Russian spacemen walked across the moon. On the basis of the Apollo program and the extensive rendezvous and docking techniques that were demanded, as well as the progressive and orderly development of both the Saturn C-5 and Nova boosters, it is my opinion that we stand scarce opportunity for success in being first on the moon.

On the basis of the lunar rendezvous technique, however, the odds are more finely balanced. I would provide to the reader a note of caution, however, with respect to the Soviet program. If the Russians have proved anything at all, it is that they make every attempt *not to repeat any one space mission* that involves manned vehicles. Rather, each step is made with a massive attempt to gain as much knowledge, skill, and experience as is possible; then, this new gathering of data serves as the base from which to leap to another high plateau of accomplishment.

If the Russians continue this line of development—despite the many formidable obstacles of docking, navigation, and re-entry at 25,000 mph still to be overcome—then the Soviet Union would see a lunar landing perhaps as early as 1965–66. If the United States is to accomplish a similar feat in this same time interval, nothing less than a crash program in terms of effort and daring decisions is an absolute necessity.

Apparently this is the course that we have chosen. The new emphasis on our man-on-the-moon effort begins almost immediately—with Project Mercury.

With each succeeding venture into space, we have grown more imaginative and certainly we have taken bolder steps. Originally, we planned that Project Mercury would entail no less than four to six three-orbit missions in space. Now, after the spectacular accomplishments of Glenn and Carpenter, we have scheduled for our third orbital flight a mission of no less than six orbits about the earth—a distinction to be gained by Astronaut Wally Schirra.

How many six-orbit flights will we make? This is impossible to answer since we had never planned for any such missions. But as we gained in experience and knowledge, we struck aside our limited progressive steps and reached out for much greater accomplishments. What happens after Schirra's space mission is entirely dependent upon the results of that mission. It may be that we shall schedule a number of these six-orbit flights, if only to gain special insight into the problems of weightlessness sustained for at least nine hours—the time period at which Gherman Titov (and the dogs orbited in Russian spacecraft) showed signs of dizziness and nausea, but which apparently did not affect to any extent cosmonauts Nikolayev and Popovich.

The fourth American mission in space may well be for 18 orbits—and 27 hours spent in the Mercury capsule around the world.

But whatever we attempt to accomplish with Mercury, Project

Gemini has already received a tremendous impetus to accelerate *that* program. Each GT mission (Gemini-Titan) will be directed toward gathering as much experience and "building blocks" of knowledge in the briefest possible time.

GT-1 will be launched unmanned in 1963 for all the preliminary activities of Gemini; this mission will check out the performance of the capsule in orbit, its new "shelving arrangement" of equipment, the checkout and launch procedure, aerodynamic and re-entry characteristics, and other areas in which we must have definitive information prior to sending the manned Gemini ships into orbit.

All things being equal—and this is presupposing that we do not encounter any disastrous problems along the way—the *second* Gemini mission will be *manned*.

Originally, NASA planned for several unmanned Gemini missions, and then initial manned orbital flights in the two-man spacecraft of perhaps one day, two days at the most.

But this cautious approach has now been scrapped. The very first time that our astronauts rocket into space aboard the Gemini spaceship, *it will be their intention to remain in space for at least seven days.*

Not only does this week-long mission—scheduled for no later than early 1964—represent a staggering forward advance in our manned space program, but it is only the prelude to another great accomplishment scheduled for the same mission. During their week in orbit, the two astronauts are scheduled to depressurize their capsule, and to leave the Gemini spaceship while in orbit. Tethered to the capsule—one man inside while one is out— the astronaut will carry out a series of tests toward effecting repairs to the exterior of the spacecraft, and studying his own reactions and abilities in terms of accomplishing rendezvous with another spacecraft.

GT-3 and GT-4 represent advances fully as comprehensive and meaningful as their predecessors. Both the third and fourth missions of the Gemini program are planned to be durations in space of fully 14 days and nights—two weeks in orbit. Again, the plan is to carry out extensive research work in orbit, and to judge with the greatest possible accuracy the capabilities of these men in the space environment.

It is planned that the new astronauts brought into the manned space program will participate in these missions as "copilots." Since Major Donald K. Slayton was removed in mid-July from any active space flights—the first man ever to be so close to, and then denied, the wonders of space flight—there are only six of the original Mercury astronauts available for the program, and this is the prime moment to begin the active in-space experience of the "second astronauts group."

The fifth Gemini mission—GT-5—represents another critical milestone. This flight will last about 48 hours, and it is during this orbital mission that our astronauts will attempt their first actual rendezvous with an Agena spacecraft.

All this, of course, is simply establishing an exhaustive and far-flung foundation for the new manned lunar landing effort— the concept of orbital rendezvous.

The decision to go to lunar rendezvous virtually tosses into the wastebasket much of the philosophy of approach toward the Apollo program. The originally accepted program called for the parallel development of the rocket boosters, stages, and modules on which we would depend for lunar landing. Briefly, in the Saturn C-5 program the plan was to use the Saturn C-5 boosters, each of 7,500,000 pounds thrust in their first stages, to orbit and rendezvous two separate components of the Apollo spaceship to land on the moon. Each Saturn booster (named Cronus) would orbit a payload of at least 100,000 pounds; the two payloads would be joined together into the lunar landing Apollo. A booster rocket would hurl the Apollo to escape velocity of about 25,000 miles per hour—and the 150,000-pound, three-module giant would be on its way to its lunar landing.

The Nova concept was different only in respect to eliminating the rendezvous plan. The enormous rocket would, instead, hurl the 150,000-pound Apollo directly to the moon from the earth's surface, without any intermediate staging or rendezvous techniques.

But all this is now—at least until events prove the NASA decision invalid, if this ever happens—tossed out the window in terms of the initial lunar flights. This point must be emphasized. The lunar orbital technique does not necessarily mean that the programs described in the earlier chapters are scrapped; it means that they are pushed aside for the immediacy of the program in favor of the new effort. NASA believes that lunar-orbit-and-landing may save two years in landing men on the moon—and actually slice 10 to 15 per cent from the over-all costs.

The new plan calls for three men to be sent in the Apollo spaceship to the vicinity of the moon. The mother ship will go into orbit about 100 miles above the lunar surface. Then, a small "lunar landing bug" carrying two men will detach from the mother ship and begin its descent to the moon, while a third astronaut remains in the command module of the Apollo space-craft as it continues to orbit the moon.

The two-man crew of the "bug" would remain on the moon's surface from two to four days. Then, carrying out a careful two-man countdown, they would ascend from the lunar surface to go into orbit about the moon—and rendezvous with the mother ship. Once the two spacecraft had docked together, the two astronauts would clamber through an airlock back into the Apollo command module. The bug would be "cast off," and the men would initiate their return to the earth—to re-enter the atmosphere in the manner described in the previous chapter.

NASA officials state emphatically that the lunar orbiting plan offers a considerably greater opportunity of success than the earth-rendezvous or direct-ascent methods, and that it retains "essentially" the same elements of safety for the astronauts in-volved. Specifically, Dr. Brainerd Holmes stated of the lunar rendezvous method that this was best for "cost, simplicity, sched-ule and minimal additional requirements."

Holmes added: "There comes a point in time when after care-ful study, you must decide which way to proceed, which will be the prime mode, which to concentrate on." Thus lunar orbit is the decision, with earth-rendezvous and direct-ascent taking "a back seat for a while."

The Saturn C-5 system with the spacecraft attached will weigh

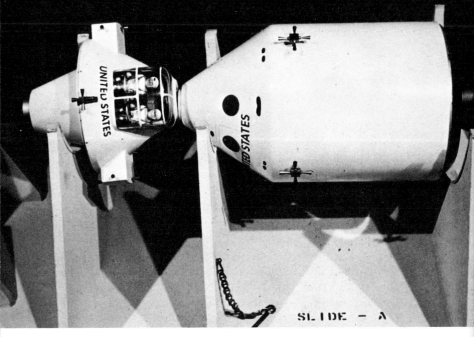

The three-module "new" Apollo spaceship as its orbits the moon. Nose-to-nose with the Apollo Command Module is the 15-ton Lunar Excursion Vehicle, with the two astronauts already in place. The Apollo Command Module is attached to its Service Propulsion Module. The Lunar Excursion ship casts free to decelerate to the moon's surface, while the Apollo "mother ship" remains in lunar orbit with one astronaut aboard.

about 6,000,000 pounds, and stand 325 feet high. The booster system will be unchanged—a first stage of five F.1 engines totaling 7,500,000 pounds thrust; a second stage of five J.2 engines totaling 1,000,000 pounds thrust; and a third stage of a single J.2 engine of 200,000 pounds thrust.

The Apollo Command Module will remain in its present size of 13 feet wide and 12 feet high. It will weigh about five tons, and will house the three-man astronaut crew.

The Service Module will weigh 23 tons and will stand 23 feet high. It will contain the propellant and propulsion systems for all necessary midcourse corrections, lunar orbit maneuvers, and return to earth.

Finally, there will be the lunar excursion vehicle, which will weigh about 15 tons and stand 20 feet tall.

The Saturn C-5 launch vehicle system will fire from the earth's surface directly to a velocity of about 25,000 miles per hour. It will be placed on a course to the moon. When it reaches the vicinity of the moon, after necessary midcourse corrections from the Service Module, the latter module will fire its rockets to enter orbit about the moon at a height of 100 miles.

In lunar orbit, the Apollo Command Module and the lunar bug would be nose-to-nose. As the Apollo orbited about the lunar equator, two astronauts would leave the Command Module by airlock, and enter their lunar landing craft.

The next step is to separate the two vehicles. The two-man crew would use reaction jets to position their 15-ton spacecraft to the exact attitude desired, and fire a brief burst of power to slow down their orbital speed.

The new orbit entered into by the landing spacecraft would take it as low as ten miles above the moon's surface. Sitting in a glass-enclosed capsule, the two astronauts would search care-

The Lunar Excursion Vehicle ascending from the moon's surface. Left behind on the moon is the moon-base vehicle used for the landing. The two-man Bug moves into orbit with the Apollo mother ship to rendezvous and dock for crew transfer. The astronauts return to the Apollo Command Module, cast the Bug free as a lunar-orbiting derelict, and begin the long trip back to earth.

fully for what appears to be the best possible place for descending to the moon. When the landing site is selected, the men would use computers to determine their subsequent flight maneuvers. The rockets would be fired again to decelerate the vehicle, beginning the actual descent to the surface.

Finally the bug would be descending vertically. For several seconds it would hover directly over the moon's surface, while spiderlike legs extended out and downward for the actual landing. Then, the thrust would be slightly reduced, and the spacecraft would settle to the moon itself.

The astronauts would then explore the moon for a period of two to four days, depending upon any possible malfunctions that might be encountered.

The next step—the most critical of the entire mission—is to return to the lunar orbit (a coplanar orbit) in order to rendezvous with the Apollo spaceship at 100 miles.

There is still no decision—the answer must be determined by experience with the Gemini flights—as to whether a "soft docking" or "hard docking" technique would be employed for the actual rendezvous. In the case of soft docking, the astronauts would bring the two spacecraft into close proximity. A line would be passed from one spacecraft to the other, and the two astronauts would use the line as a guide to return to the Apollo.

With hard docking, the two ships would be returned to their former nose-to-nose position, and be mechanically coupled. The astronauts would re-enter the Apollo through the Command Module airlock.

Whatever rendezvous technique is used, the next step is to cast free the lunar landing vehicle, and leave it as a derelict in lunar orbit. Another countdown would ensue within the Apollo Command Module. Working closely with computer information radioed from earth, the astronauts would establish a careful attitude of the big spaceship. With everything in time, attitude, and position in lunar orbit carefully established, the spacemen would fire the 20,000-pound-thrust rocket engine of their Service Module, to begin the return to earth.

Obviously, any such venture that demands so many maneuvers is one fraught with all possible sources of danger.

First, the required reliability of all equipment is staggering. Any failure of major equipment could doom the mission. There is always the chance—and it is not as remote as some people would like it to be—that only one man might return from lunar orbit. The dangers inherent in the landing maneuvers, as well as successful ascent and rendezvous, are too great to be ignored.

Because of these dangers, NASA also is investigating other methods for the lunar exploration program. One, receiving the highest consideration, is to develop a "lunar logistics vehicle." This would be an unmanned robot that would be sent to the moon before the manned craft, to carry extensive supplies, tools, and special equipment which the lunar landing astronauts might find indispensable to their survival.

It is important to note that from all that may be learned of the Soviet program, the lunar logistics-vehicle plan—but including several such unmanned spacecraft—is the method on which the Russians have been concentrating their energy. In this respect, their large rocket-booster development may well give them a commanding lead to effect such a program before we ourselves are ready to do so.

NASA doesn't wish to avoid any possible schemes—so long as they are practicable—for reaching the moon in the shortest possible time.

One of them is the possible use of the two-man Gemini spaceship for a circumlunar flight about the moon. If rendezvous and docking work out as we hope it will, then the Gemini spaceship would be able to carry out a two-man circumlunar flight by 1965.

By that time we will be orbiting the three-ton Gemini spaceships as a matter of course. The Saturn C-1 booster will be able to place 20,000-pound payloads into orbit, and the C-1B will orbit 32,000 pounds. The rendezvous and docking of powered rocket stages would permit the Gemini to be boosted to escape velocity, carry out midcourse guidance corrections, swing around the moon back toward the earth, and, finally, decelerate to orbital speed or less for re-entry. The entire flight would take from five to seven days—well within the capabilities of the two-man spacecraft designed to orbit the earth for 14 days.

Also under accelerated study for the Saturn C-5 booster-vehicle system would be a flight system that involves the earth-rendezvous technique for the two-man lunar landing ship, and especially, the two-man ship that would make the direct ascent to the moon from the earth's surface.

If the two-man spaceship system is used in earth-rendezvous, much time could be saved by adapting new module designs around the Gemini. This spacecraft would be cramped and uncomfortable, perhaps, but comfort is not one of the intended requirements of the initial lunar exploration missions. And the lunar landing could be accomplished in this fashion.

One NASA plan that revolves around the two-man spaceship —with direct flight to the moon—calls for advancing the power of the Saturn C-5 booster vehicle. This could be accomplished with less delay than would ordinarily be encountered, by making the C-5 a six-engine first-stage booster, or adapting the M-1 engine of 1,200,000 pounds thrust for the second stage.

One discordant note has been struck in the formulation of these new plans. The enormous Nova booster is being delayed in its development by at least two years. NASA feels the delay will be well worthwhile. Nova is not essential to the initial exploration of the moon, and the added development time will be used to increase the lifting power of this giant by at least 50 per cent—so that Nova can send into a low earth orbit a *payload* of more than 600,000 pounds on a single flight!

From all these new plans and activities, there emerges a new note, an undercurrent in our nation's lunar exploration program. That undercurrent is one of urgency. It may be that we will not realize our goal to be first on the surface of the moon, that the Soviet headstart will be too much to overcome. Be that as it may, it is essential that every American understand that, if nothing else, we have signaled "Full speed ahead" in our lunar landing program.

Index